14-120-750

Electricity

AND

Electronics

BASIC

WILLIAM B. STEINBERG
Supervisor of Industrial Arts
San Diego City Schools

WALTER B. FORD
Professor, Electricity – Radio
Industrial Arts Department
San Diego State College

AMERICAN TECHNICAL SOCIETY · CHICAGO, U.S.A.

PREFACE

"Atomic Age" is the name often applied to the period in which we live. It is also frequently referred to as the "Air Age" and in similar terms that emphasize the importance of science and invention in our time. But we can speak of an age that has prepared the way for these and includes them all—the "Age of Electricity and Electronics."

From the awe-inspiring achievements of nuclear science and the spectacular advancements in aviation to the innumerable discoveries that have added comfort and convenience to our daily lives, we are constantly dependent upon electricity and electronics. You may never operate an atom-smasher or guide a space ship, but if electric lights, the automobile, the telephone, radio, or television enter into your activities you need to know something about the basic principles that are utilized in all of these.

Anyone who wishes to feel at home in the world of modern technology must be familiar with the fundamentals of electricity and electronics. To make it possible to acquire this familiarity quickly and easily is the purpose of this book. The necessary information is presented in a direct and simple manner. Each step is clearly illustrated by photographs and drawings.

As you proceed through the text you will gradually learn the convenient symbols used by engineers and technicians in all fields to represent electrical and electronic equipment on diagrams. At the end of each unit of study, there is a group of "Review Questions." These are provided to assist the reader to test his knowledge and to check his progress.

"Interesting Things to Do" is what the authors have called the many fascinating projects that enable you to demonstrate and apply what you learn in the text. These projects are not only interesting but produce useful articles and develop practical skills. Few tools are necessary and generally only materials commonly found in a home or school shop are required.

The knowledge of electricity and electronics gained from this book will open up new and inviting paths. A great number of vocational opportunities exist and they are multiplying rapidly in the area that is leading progress in most occupational fields. A variety of exciting hobbies offer themselves. And you will have the keen satisfaction of grasping the essentials of an important part of your everyday life.

CONTENTS

THIS ELECTRICAL AND ELECTRONIC AGE

MAKING USE OF MAGNETISM

HOW ELECTRICITY IS PRODUCED

BASIC ELECTRICAL CIRCUITS

ELECTRICITY FOR EVERYDAY LIVING

USING ELECTRICITY FOR COMMUNICATION

BASIC ELECTRICAL FORMULAS

STANDARD SYMBOLS FOR ELECTRONICS

SOLDERING HINTS

SUPPLEMENTARY PROJECTS

INDEX

INTERESTING THINGS TO DO

MAKING USE OF MAGNETISM

HOW ELECTRICITY IS PRODUCED

BASIC ELECTRICAL CIRCUITS

ELECTRICITY FOR EVERYDAY LIVING

USING ELECTRICITY FOR COMMUNICATION

SUPPLEMENTARY PROJECTS

ELECTRONICS EXPLORES THE STARS

This hypersensitive antenna is used to pick up radiations from outer space to tell us more about the vast universe in which we live.

This Electrical

and

Electronic Age

~~~~~~~~~~~~~~~~~~~~~~~~~~~~~~~~~~~~

UNIT 1

THINGS ELECTRICITY CAN DO

Electricity and Electronics

It is very difficult to separate the meaning of the two words *electricity* and *electronics*. The field of electricity is usually thought of as electricity that is used in magnets, generators, motors, lights, and heaters.

The field of electronics is usually thought of as electricity that is used in radio, television, and other equipment where electron tubes and transistors are needed.

In the Home

We are so accustomed to flipping a switch in our homes and having a room instantly flooded with light that we seldom think of what is happening behind the scenes to make this possible. Yet back of every home lighting system there are a number of interesting devices. The names of these devices are strange to most of us. As we proceed with the study of electricity we shall become very familiar with the names and the electrical equipment they represent and learn what an important part they play in bringing electricity into our homes.

Probably the most important use of electricity in the modern home is for producing light, either by the common light bulb or fluorescent lamps. In addition to furnishing light, electric lamps of the ultraviolet type can bring the effects of sunshine into the home

Courtesy San Diego Gas and Electric Co.

◆ 1. Portable radio equipment is used to speed up construction of power lines that bring the benefits of electricity to all areas.

and also kill harmful germs in the air. Electric lamps of the infrared type can provide us with the effects of radiant heat.

How many electric motors are working in your home to lighten household tasks and provide for your comfort? If you gave an answer offhand without stopping to count them you would probably fall far short of the correct number. In the average modern home electric motors operate the clothes washer and drier, refrigerator, garbage disposal, fan, electric razor, clock, furnace blower, and workshop equipment. And if we include the family automobile, we can add to the above list, starter motor, and many other motor-driven accessories that are being installed on modern automobiles. The uses for electricity in the home do not end with furnishing light and motor power. Electrical heating provides for the comfort of the family by operating the range, toaster, waffle iron, water heater, coffee maker, heating pad, iron and ironer, clothes drier and electric blanket. And while the tubes in our radio and television sets appear as dimly lighted electric lamps and are not classed as heating devices, the operation of the tube also depends upon the heat given off by its filament.

On the Farm

Electricity is just as important to the

◆ 2. Amateur radio is a fascinating hobby. A knowledge of electronics will help you to qualify for a government license to operate your own station.

farm as it is to the modern city dwelling. About two-thirds of all farms use electricity to lighten the chores as well as to serve in the home. Many of the jobs that were formerly done by hand and required many man-hours may now be done with electricity in a fraction of the time. These include pumping water, grinding feed, milking, shearing sheep, hoisting hay and feed, and many of the other jobs which are found around a farm.

In Industry and Business

When we think of the many ways in which electricity helps to run a modern home, we are apt to overlook the part it plays in keeping the wheels of industry going. Actually, only about one-third of all of the electricity produced in our power plants is used by farms and homes. The remaining two-thirds supplies the needs of commercial and industrial plants. The average workman today in a modern manufacturing plant uses in the machines which he operates over 10,000 kilowatt-hours of electrical energy a year. Stated in terms that are more easily understood, this means that he uses enough electrical energy to supply seven or eight modern homes during the year. Let us consider some of the ways in which this tremendous amount of electricity is used in industry.

In the great steel industries electricity is used in practically every process from the time the crude iron ore is taken from the earth to when the finished product in the form of flat steel sheets is ready for delivery to manufacturing plants across the nation. Electric shovels are used to dig the ore and electric cranes load it into freight cars or ships and unload it again at the steel plant. Electric conveyers carry it to the blast furnaces in which the iron is changed into steel.

Courtesy Philco Corp.

◆ 3. The United States Air Force has perfected a far-seeing "third eye"—airborne television. Now the military command can watch the TV screen as though it were a living, moving map.

The rolls which form the steel into sheets are driven by electric motors. When the finished sheets of steel reach the manufacturing plants, electric motors operate the machines which shape them into some of the appliances that contribute so much to our way of living. These electric motors help produce radio and television chassis, and many of the small appliances found in the home. Aluminum, which has done so much toward lightening our daily tasks, could probably not be made without electricity. The only practical way in which aluminum can be separated from the ore is by an electrical process.

For Communication

Primitive man depended upon fire, smoke, or drum signals to send his thoughts to his neighbor. Modern man has only to lift the receiver of his tele-

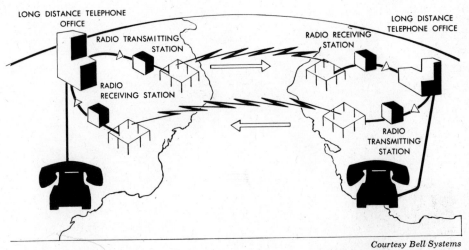

Courtesy Bell Systems

◆ **4. This is a schematic diagram of a trans-oceanic radiotelephone link that enables you** to **call foreign lands from your own home.**

phone and dial a series of numbers to send his voice to the most distant point of our nation. And with little more effort he can talk with someone in some distant foreign land or on a ship thousands of miles from our shores. See Diagram 4.

All of this is made possible by the magic of electricity working through our land telephone lines and domestic and foreign radiotelephone stations.

For Lighting

Not very long ago we were limited in our working and playing time to the hours of daylight. In order to make the greatest use of their plants, many modern industries operate on a 24-hour schedule, which only adequate electric lighting makes possible. While the largest electric lamp in the home rarely provides more than a few hundred candlepower of light, the lamps used in industry are rated in terms of thousands of candlepower. In the field of recreation, electric lighting has made it possible for athletes to perform after dark and for spectators to enjoy the contests.

For Automation

The word *automation* has become a common one in industry. By means of automation, complete manufacturing processes are performed entirely automatically. With electric timing devices and relays, many jobs which were formerly done by hand power are now being done with electricity. Automation makes it possible to do these jobs without the mistakes that a man might make if he were operating a machine. It permits much-needed manpower to be used elsewhere. Many industrial plants are now being automatically made ready for the day's operation before the first worker appears on the job in the morning. See Illustration 5.

7:20 A.M. STARTS MOTORS IN COMPRESSORS TO BUILD UP PRESSURE

7:30 A.M. TURNS ON LIGHTS IN CORRIDORS AND LOCKER ROOMS

7:15 A.M. SWITCHES ON OVENS AND PLATING BATHS

7:40 A.M. TURNS ON LIGHTS IN MAIN PLANT

7:00 A.M. TURNS UP HEAT OR AIR CONDITIONING

7:55 A.M. TURNS ON POWER FOR MACHINE TOOLS

8:00 A.M. SOUNDS STARTING SIGNAL

Courtesy IBM

◆ 5. Up to 40 remote operations—lights, motors, heating and air conditioning systems, as well as clocks, time recorders and signals—can be automatically controlled by a central control system. Before the plant opens . . . during the working day . . . after close-down, the electronic control system will maintain automatic and efficient 24-hour supervision.

In Research

Little could be done in a modern research laboratory without the aid of electricity. Nearly all of the measuring devices used in developing nuclear power for the use of mankind are electrically operated. Geiger counters which detect the presence of uranium ores in the field are run with batteries. X-ray machines, which depend upon electricity for operation, are used in industry to detect flaws in metal castings, as well as for medical purposes. With travel in outer space almost a

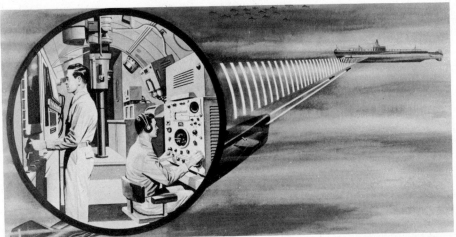

Courtesy Bendix

♦ 6. Reflected sound waves are used to show the location of an enemy submarine. The safety of the nation depends upon electronics.

certainty in the future, scientists are now engaged in collecting information from the upper regions, such as the strength and direction of winds, temperatures, density of the atmosphere, humidity, and gravitational pull of the earth. Most of this information is obtained by means of balloons and rockets. In some cases small battery-operated radio transmitters are sent up into the air to send the information back to earth. Sometimes small parachutes are released from the rocket or balloon at a certain altitude to bring back information which has been recorded on delicate electrically operated instruments. Much of today's scientific research requires the solving of difficult mathematical problems, some of which would require days to solve by the usual methods. Electrically operated computers now make the answers to these available in seconds.

In the Military

Electrical developments for military uses have kept pace with the progress for peacetime applications. While many of the new devices must be classified as secret, the world at large knows that our coast lines are protected by a screen of radar to warn against any hostile attack; that our guided missiles are capable of seeking out and destroying an enemy aircraft long before it could reach our shores.

REVIEW QUESTIONS

1. List the ways in which you have used electricity since getting out of bed this morning.

2. Make a list of the number of electric motors that you have in your home.

3. What is the size of the largest

lamp used for lighting in your home?

4. Name several uses for the electric lamp.

5. How are electric motors used in manufacturing plants?

6. What part of all of the electric power produced is used by farms and homes?

7. Which metal depends upon an electrical process for its manufacture?

8. What is meant by the word *automation?*

9. How do scientists learn about conditions in the upper atmosphere?

10. Tell how electricity is used to protect our shores from invasion by another country.

UNIT 2
FUTURE DEVELOPMENTS IN ELECTRONICS

In the Home

What does the future hold for us in new electrical and electronic developments? We can almost rub our lamp like Aladdin, make a wish for some new electrical development, and be reasonably certain that our electronics and electrical laboratories can produce it. The research laboratories are working constantly to produce a more efficient lamp. Perhaps in the not too distant future we shall have a really "cold" electric light.

The wall switch for controlling lights in the home as we know it today may give way to a device which does

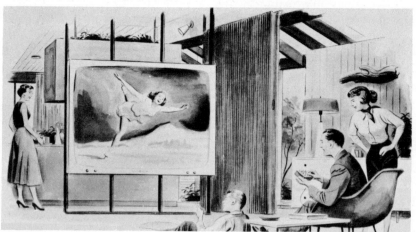

Courtesy General Electric Co.

◆ 7. A practical method of direct light amplification may be the key to large-screen television sets, which are thin enough to hang on a wall or to be used as room dividers.

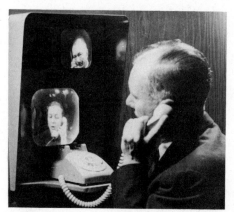

Courtesy Kay Laboratory

◆ 8. A television telephone that will make it possible to see the person at the other end of the line.

the same thing when one merely waves a hand toward the lamp to be controlled. A similar type of device may be used for protecting the home against unwanted intruders. Ultrasonic sound waves, which are generated electrically, fill a room. Any movement of an object or person within the room, however slight, may change the pitch of the sound wave and cause electrical relays to sound an alarm. In the entertainment field we may look for a flat wall screen to replace our present television tube, as shown in Illustration 7. The development of the "light amplifier" has made this possible, and it should be but a short time until it becomes a commercial reality.

The television telephone by which one may see the person to whom he is speaking has already been developed. See Photograph 8. This may soon be put into general use.

In Industry

In the industrial field we shall prob-

Courtesy Westinghouse Electric Corp.

◆ 9. In the future electricity will be produced in power plants using atomic energy as the fuel.

Courtesy Jet Propulsion Laboratory

◆ 10. Using radio waves to follow the operation of a rocket. A process called *telemetering* is used to record the information from a rocket, as shown by the tape at the sides of the picture.

ably see automation take over more and more of the operations which are now done by manual labor. Perhaps we shall see a whole manufacturing operation from the raw material to the finished product, built entirely by means of electrically controlled machinery. Human attention will be required only to keep it operating in correct working order.

Many new developments are possible with the use of radar. One of these is the automatic control of automobiles on the highways. We may one day see automobiles traveling safely along our roads steered solely by means of radar. The same principles will be applied to controlling our airplanes. Radar will guide them safely to their destinations, from take-off to landing, without the aid of human hands.

A journey into space may be an adventure of the future. The construction of space ships that can travel to other planets is now being studied. When the time comes for these space ships to be built, electronics will play a most important part in their operation.

REVIEW QUESTIONS

1. What new electrical device can you think of that might be developed for the home?

2. Explain what is meant by "cold" electric lighting.

3. For what purposes, other than lighting, can electric lamps be used?

4. What new development may replace our present day television tube?

5. What electronic device may someday be used to make highway travel safer?

UNIT 3
OPPORTUNITIES IN ELECTRICITY AND ELECTRONICS

Electricity and Electronics as a Vocation

Probably no other industry provides better job opportunities than the field of electricity and electronics. New electronic developments are made almost every day, and each of these developments provides new jobs. Everywhere we look, electricity and electronics are being used more and more. The tremendous growth of electrical devices means that more people are needed to design, install, and repair these items.

Jobs in the field of electricity and electronics may be divided into four groups: construction, service and repair, communications, and design and research.

Construction Work

Construction work includes jobs done by the electrician who does house wiring, the lineman who installs electrical power lines and telegraph lines, and other types of electricians who install electrical circuits in such places

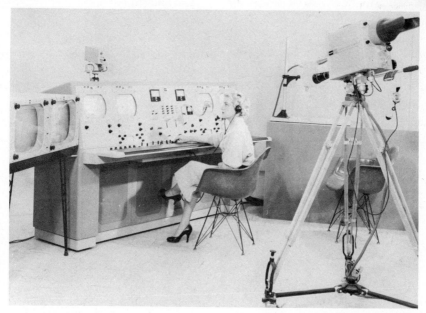

Courtesy Kay Laboratory

◆ 11. Control panel and portable camera used with closed circuit television installations in industrial plants. Closed circuit television is today saving time and money in plants throughout the nation. The operation at several points in a plant may be observed at the same time through the use of portable TV cameras.

Courtesy Radio Corporation of America

◆ 12. Making the final tests on an ultra-high-frequency transmitter before it is shipped from the plant.

Service and Repair Work

Service and repair work includes such jobs as the repair of motors, generators, household electrical appliances, radio receivers, amplifiers, television sets, and electronic computers. The electrical appliance repairman is an all-around mechanic who can wind motors, repair toasters, and install small electrical machinery. Radio and television repairmen need to be familiar with all of the different sets being manufactured and have to be able to use many types of test equipment.

Electronics technicians repair and test special equipment, including computing machines, electronic controls, electronic indicators, and other types of special devices. They are usually specialists on certain types of equipment. Some install electronic equipment used for military purposes.

Service and repair workers must have a very good understanding of

as manufacturing plants, mines, and airplanes. Most electricians are specialists who are trained to do certain jobs. Each job requires training in a particular field of electrical work.

For these jobs one needs a basic understanding of electrical circuits. The ability to read electrical blueprints is necessary and information about the safety requirements in electrical installations is very important. High school courses in electricity and radio, mathematics, and science are very valuable. Most jobs require a period of training as an apprentice or as an electrician's helper—in addition to the fine courses in electricity, radio, mathematics, and science that are available in most communities.

Courtesy Western Union

◆ 13. Facsimile equipment used in modern telegraph installations which transmits anything that can be put on paper. Handwriting, typewriting, printed matter, and photographs can be sent between any points connected by wire or radio.

◆ 14. Operating a computer or "magic brain" that is electronically controlled. Scientists use this equipment to solve difficult mathematical problems.

electronics principles. Developing this understanding may start with high school courses in mathematics, science, electricity, and radio. Additional training may be obtained at a vocational school, junior college, or college. Because of the technical type of equipment on electronic devices many manufacturers have special training courses on the use and repair of their own equipment.

Communications Work

Communications work includes such jobs as operating and maintaining radio broadcast stations, television stations, radar stations, telephone relay stations, ship radio stations, and airplane radio stations. These people must be able to install, repair, and operate their equipment. For many of these jobs, it is necessary to obtain an operator's license that is issued by the government. To receive this license one must pass a written examination on the operating requirements and electronics fundamentals.

The rapid increase in the installation of transmitting equipment in vehicles such as trucks, automobiles, airplanes, and trains has provided a need for many kinds of communications workers. The use of radar to aid in making airplane travel safer has

Courtesy General Electric Co.

◆ 15. Engineers are observing the effect of 10,000,000 volts of an artificial lightning discharge.

also provided many job opportunities.

High school training in physics and mathematics is necessary for communications workers. Courses in electronics are also very helpful. Additional training at vocational schools, junior colleges, or colleges is often necessary for communications jobs.

Communications workers who are responsible for the design and installation of equipment often are college-trained electrical engineers.

Design and Research Workers

Design and research workers play an important part in our daily lives. They are responsible for many products that we use every day such as the telephone, television, and other electrical equipment. It is the design and research worker who develops the products that are used by the construction worker, the service and repair worker and the communication worker. He is, in almost all cases, a trained engineer in the field of electricity and electronics.

The electronics engineers design, test, build, operate, or supervise the construction of all kinds of electrical equipment. Much of their time is spent in research to try to find new and better electronic devices.

There are many kinds of electrical and electronics engineers. The power generation and transmission engineer designs and supervises the construction of power plants and transmission lines. The electronics and radio engineers are concerned with research and design of radar, television, and radio equipment. The illumination engineers test and design lighting equipment. Other electronics engineers are concerned with the development of electronic products.

A college education in electrical or

electronics engineering is important for the design and research worker. He should be good in the fields of mathematics and science. Courses in high school electric and radio shop and mechanical drawing are desirable. To those who have the ability, the opportunities in the field of electronics engineering seem to be unlimited.

Even within these many general areas of electrical and electronics engineering, there are specialized fields that will appeal to persons with particular interests. For example, the illumination engineer who has a keen artistic sense may find his ideal occupation in the motion picture industry or in the theater, while the electronics engineer with an appreciation of music may find his greatest opportunity in one of the many positions concerned with the recording and reproduction of high fidelity music.

REVIEW QUESTIONS

1. What field of electronics would you choose as a vocation?

2. Why should jobs in electricity and electronics be plentiful in the future?

3. List the jobs that a good service electrician should be able to do.

4. What type of electronics work requires a government license?

5. Name as many electrical or electronics engineering jobs as you can.

Making Use of Magnetism

Everyday Uses of Permanent Magnets

To understand electricity we must first know something about magnetism. *Magnetism* is not the same as electricity, but it plays a very important part in the construction and operation of many electrical devices.

Almost everyone has picked up pieces of iron with a magnet or has seen a small magnet hold itself to a metal surface. This simple principle, of holding on to certain metals, is used for many practical purposes around the home. The tack hammer shown in Illustration 1 is a magnet used to hold tacks firmly to the hammer head so that the user will not have to hold the tacks

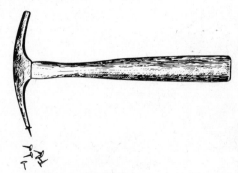

◆ 1. The magnetic tack hammer is a very useful tool for upholstering or where tacks must be driven in hard-to-get-at places. The magnetic head is usually in a horseshoe form and the opposite end of the head is non-magnetic.

with his fingers. In the kitchen, magnets are attached to potholders so that

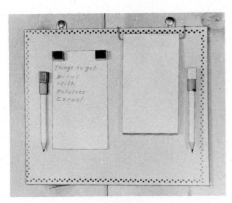

◆ 2. This note pad holder consists of a steel backplate and several small permanent magnets. These magnets hold paper and pencils when placed on the metal back.

they will "stick" to the stove, refrigerator, or other metal surfaces. Magnetic strips are used to hold sharp knives, small magnets hold notes to a metal plate on cabinet doors (Photograph 2), and cabinet doors are held closed with magnets. Some games use magnets to keep miniature players on a metal playing board.

All around us magnets are used; however, most people do not know how materials are magnetized. Illustrations 1, 2, and 3 are examples of how some permanent magnets are used. They are really artificial magnets because they were not magnets in their

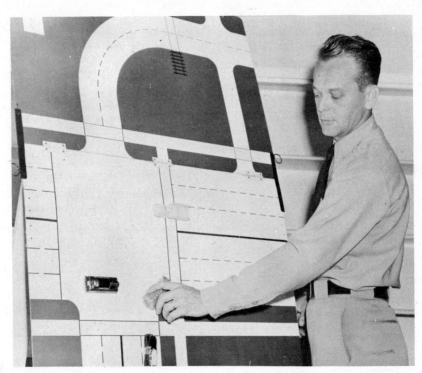

◆ 3. In traffic courts, magnets in miniature plastic automobiles will hold the vehicles to a metal board so that positions of various automobiles that have been involved in an accident may be illustrated.

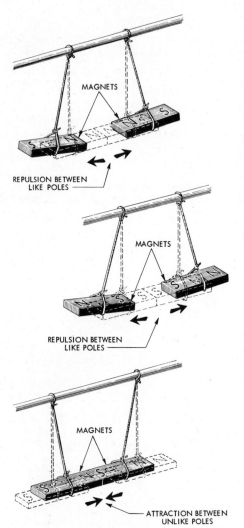

♦ 5. The top magnets were placed so that the like poles were near each other. When iron filings were sprinkled on them, a pattern formed, which shows that the two like magnetic fields push each other away. In the lower magnets, with unlike poles placed close together, the magnets have a strong attraction for each other. The iron filings form the path of the magnetic field.

Magnetic Action

If the ends of two bar magnets are placed near each other, they will either pull together or stay apart. See Illustrations 4 and 5. We can easily see that the ends marked alike tend to repel each other, and those marked unlike tend to attract each other. The *N* and *S* on the bars are commonly called *poles* and are referred to as the *north pole* and the *south pole* of the magnet. With this information, we can now state the first principle of magnetism: *Like poles repel each other and unlike poles attract each other.*

♦ 4. When the ends marked *N* are brought together, there is a tendency for the two bars to move apart or push each other away. The same is true if the ends marked *S* are brought together. Now if the end of one bar marked *N* is brought near the end of the other bar marked *S*, the two bars will pull themselves together.

natural form. Something had to be done to the material to change it into a magnet.

◆ 6. The ball bearings shown in the photograph represent the molecules in a piece of steel. A magnetized piece of steel has all of the molecules aligned so that the like poles are all in the same direction.

◆ 7. Each ball or molecule is marked to show that it has a north and south pole. In this unmagnetized piece of steel the molecules are not arranged in an orderly pattern.

Structure of Magnets

Not all pieces of steel are magnets. Two pieces may look exactly alike but one may attract other steel objects and one may not. The one that attracts another steel object is called a *magnet*. What makes the difference between the magnetized and unmagnetized pieces of steel?

Steel, like all things, is composed of very small particles called *molecules*. It is believed that each molecule has a north and a south pole the same as a whole magnet. In a piece of steel that is magnetized, these very small magnets have arranged themselves in an orderly fashion. Photograph 6 illustrates how the molecules have been arranged so that all north poles point in the same direction and, of course, all south poles will be pointing in the opposite direction. In the unmagnetized steel the molecules are arranged in a very irregular manner, as shown in Photograph 7. In this random arrangement of the tiny magnets, they tend to neutralize each other and thus the steel is unmagnetized.

Magnetic Induction

The unmagnetized steel may be magnetized if we stroke it with a magnet, as demonstrated in Photograph 8. The magnet will make the tiny molecules arrange themselves so that all of the poles bear in the same direction. This is called *magnetic induction*.

Magnetic Compass

If a piece of magnetized steel is suspended and left free to rotate, it will turn so that one end points north and

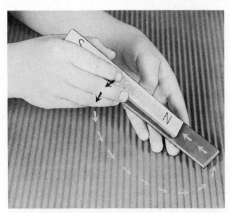

◆ 8. This piece of steel is being magnetized by stroking it with a permanent magnet. One pole of the permanent magnet is placed at one end of the piece of steel and pulled the full length of the steel. At the end of the stroke the magnet is lifted away from the steel and before starting the second stroke the magnet is again placed at the original starting position. After repeating this several times the steel will become magnetized. This is called *magnetic induction*.

the other end points south. This is because the earth is a huge magnet with north and south poles that attract the poles of the suspended magnet. This is the principle of the *magnetic compass.* The compass uses a very light, thin magnet that rotates freely on its pivot. The end of the compass that points north is commonly referred to as the *north-seeking* pole. The magnetic compass is an important aid to all types of navigation. Through its use, ships at sea are guided safely to port, explorers are protected from becoming lost, and airplanes are kept on their course.

The first compasses made by man centuries ago used a piece of *lodestone,* which means "leading stone." It is an iron ore that is naturally magnetic.

The north magnetic pole is not always in the same position; it shifts slightly from year to year. It is in the vicinity of Hudson Bay in northern Canada, as indicated in Photograph 9. The changes in location of the poles are quite small and for most purposes the pole is considered to be approximately 12° west of the geographical north when a compass is read in New York City, and approximately 18° east

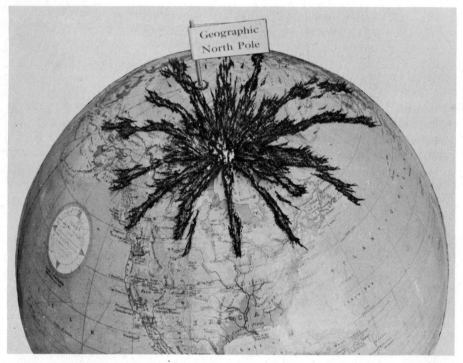

◆ 9. The iron filings on the top of the globe illustrate the magnetic field of the earth. Not everyone realizes that the earth's geographic north pole and its magnetic pole are not the same. They are approximately 1400 miles apart and the compass points to the magnetic pole. The fact that these two poles are not the same makes it necessary for air or sea navigators to recognize this difference when plotting courses.

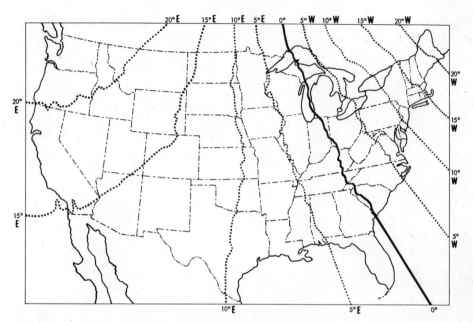

◆ 10. With this chart you will be able to determine the variation from true north that is indicated by a compass in your locality.

of the geographical north when read in San Francisco. In a narrow strip through the United States, from Michigan to Georgia, the compass will point true north and south all of the time, because the magnetic pole is directly in line with the north pole. See Illustration 10. The difference between true north and the compass reading at any place on the earth is called *variation*.

A permanent magnet may lose its magnetism by being hammered, dropped, or heated. All of these means cause the molecules to change their positions and thus the steel will lose its magnetism. On the other hand, an ordinary piece of steel will acquire magnetism if it is pointed north and hammered. The attraction of the earth's magnetism aligns the molecules.

Metals That Make Magnets

Permanent magnets are made in many shapes and sizes, as seen in Photograph 11. The common types are *horseshoe* and *bar* magnets. They are made of hardened steel, because it retains its magnetism for a long period of time. Soft steel can easily be magnetized but will not hold its magnetism. It is believed that soft steel loses its magnetism easily because the molecules of steel are free to move and thus change position readily. In hard steel the molecules are not so free to move.

A steel alloy, which is steel mixed with other metals such as tungsten, chromium, cobalt, or nickel, will make a very strong permanent magnet. Recent developments in the use of alloy steels have produced magnets which

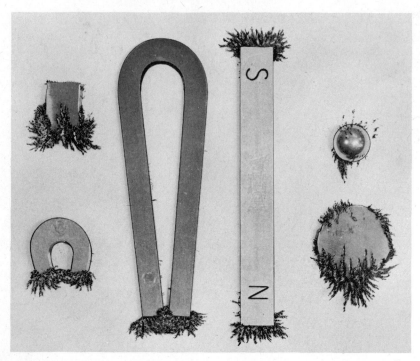

◆ 11. **Typical examples of commercial magnets. Each magnet has definite north and south poles regardless of its shape.**

have a much greater magnetic field than the hard steel magnets. One of the best alloys for making magnets contains aluminum, nickel, and cobalt. This type of alloy is commonly called *alnico*. Uses for permanent magnets other than those shown in the illustrations are in radio speakers, electrical measuring instruments, telephone receivers, generators, and motors. We shall learn more about these uses later.

Magnetic Materials

Metals which are attracted by a magnet are called *magnetic materials*. These are iron, from which steel is made, cobalt, and nickel. Other metals, including pure aluminum and copper,

zinc, and lead will not be attracted by a magnet and are called nonmagnetic. Materials other than metals, such as wood, textiles, etc., are never magnetic.

Magnetic Field

Magnetism will pass through all materials which are nonmagnetic. This can be illustrated by placing a piece of paper or glass on top of a magnet and sprinkling iron filings on it. The iron filings will become magnetized and drawn toward the magnet even though the paper or glass is between the filings and the magnet. Photograph 12 shows how the filings will form a definite pattern which is similar to the invisible magnetic field produced by the magnet. This magnetic field is always present around any magnet.

We can get a stronger magnetic field if two unlike poles are brought closer together. The closer the two poles are together without touching each other, the shorter the path will be for the magnetic field to travel. Each pole will have a greater attraction for the other and also they will have a stronger pull for other magnetic materials. If we should bend a bar magnet into the shape of a horseshoe, we would then find the magnetic field to be stronger.

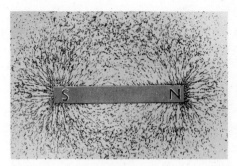

◆ 12. The iron filings show the lines of force that are always present between the poles of any magnet.

INTERESTING THINGS TO DO

1. Showing the Magnetic Field Surrounding a Single Magnet.

a. Place a bar magnet on a flat wooden surface and cover it with a sheet of paper. Sprinkle iron filings on the top of the paper and tap it lightly until a pattern forms. You now have the picture of a magnetic field. Observe that the lines tend to go from one pole to the other. Also note that the strongest field is close to the ends of the poles.

b. Sprinkle iron filings on a horseshoe magnet covered with a sheet of paper. You will notice that the magnetic field is now concentrated between the two poles. Why is there a greater magnetic field shown by the horseshoe magnet than by the bar magnet?

2. Showing the Magnetic Field Formed by Two Magnets.

a. Place two bar magnets on a flat surface, end to end, so that the north poles are approximately 1″ apart. Cover the bars with a sheet of paper and sprinkle iron filings on the paper

the same as in *1a*. Observe the pattern of the magnetic field. What is happening to the magnetic field?

b. Place two bar magnets on a flat surface, end to end, so that the north pole of one and the south pole of the other are approximately 1″ apart. Cover the bars with a sheet of paper and sprinkle iron filings on the paper. Observe the pattern of the magnets. How does it differ from the pattern of *2a*?

3. Making a Permanent Magnet by Induction.

a. Place an old hacksaw blade in a vise and with a pliers break off a piece about 2″ long. (To avoid having the blade break into several pieces do not let it extend over $2\frac{1}{2}$″ beyond the vise jaw.) Obtain a permanent magnet and stroke the blade with the magnet. Test the blade to see if it is magnetic by trying to pick up some small nails. Why has the blade become a permanent magnet?

b. Obtain two ¼″ straight-shank twist drills, and magnetize them by induction, using a very strong magnet. Be sure to stroke each drill with the same pole of the magnet and keep each drill pointed in the same direction. Then place the two drills parallel on a flat surface about ⅛″ apart. Keep the sharpened ends pointed in the same direction. Observe what happens to the drills. Why do the drills push each other apart? Reverse the direction of one of the drills. What happens and why?

4. Making a Compass.

Obtain a piece of spring steel approximately ³⁄₁₆″ wide and 1″ long (an old clock spring is excellent for this purpose). Shape the spring to a point on one end. Center-punch the spring in the middle so that it will balance on a pivot. It is easier to balance the compass if the center of the spring is raised as in Photograph 13. The pivot can be made by sharpening a brad on each end and forcing one end into a block of wood. The wood block should be about ¾″ thick and 1½″ square. A small hole can be made in the block with another brad, making it possible

◆ **13. Compass Constructed from a Clock Spring**

to push the pointed pivot in with your fingers. A drawing of the points of the compass can be made on a piece of paper and glued to the block. Magnetize the spring steel by induction. Place the magnetized spring on the pivot. If it does not balance, grind the heavy end until the steel compass needle balances perfectly. Compare the direction in which the spring points with that of a standard compass. Why does it point towards the north magnetic pole? What happens if the north pole of a bar magnet is brought near the north-seeking pole of the compass?

REVIEW QUESTIONS

1. List the uses that have been made of permanent magnets in your home.

2. Why are man-made permanent magnets called artificial magnets?

3. What are the poles of a magnet called?

4. State the basic law of magnetism.

5. When a piece of steel becomes magnetized what change takes place?

6. What is meant by *magnetic induction?*

7. What do we call the end of the compass that points towards the north?

8. What is the difference between the geographic north pole and the magnetic north pole?

9. Explain why a compass is important to all types of navigation.

10. Find out the approximate compass variation for your locality.

11. Why does the compass point true north and south in certain locations?

12. Why does hard steel retain magnetism?

13. What materials are used in making very strong permanent magnets?

14. List some nonmagnetic materials.

15. What is meant by a *magnetic field?*

16. What material did ancient navigators use for a compass?

UNIT 5
ELECTROMAGNETS

How Permanent Magnets Are Made

We have discussed how a permanent magnet may be made by stroking a section of hard steel with another magnet. Another method of making a permanet magnet is by *electromagnetism.* If insulated wire is wrapped around a hard piece of steel and the two ends of the coil are then connected to a source of electricity, such as a battery, we have what is called an *electromagnet.* If the battery is left connected for a short time, the steel will become magnetized and, when withdrawn from the coil, will be found to be a magnet.

Coil Polarity

What caused the coil of wire to magnetize the steel? We can find out if, after removing the steel core from the coil, we reconnect the coil to a battery source of electricity. Now iron filings may be sprinkled around the coil and a pattern will develop like that shown by the bar magnet. A compass may be placed near the coil and it will point

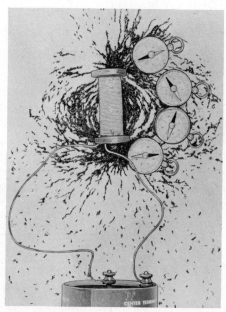

◆ 14. Compasses have been placed in the magnetic field of a coil that has been connected to a dry cell. Each compass points in the direction of the magnetic field. We can see that one end of the coil attracts the south pole of the compass. This shows us that the coil has definite north and south poles the same as a bar magnet.

in the direction of the magnetic field. See Photograph 14. This field can also be called the *lines of force*. The lines of force around the coil have a north and south pole just like the permanent magnet. The south pole of the coil will attract the north pole of the compass.

Importance of Electromagnets

Of all the functions of electricity, one of the most important is in the *electromagnet*. Many devices use the principle of electromagnetism in their construction. Without its use our entire industrial world would stop functioning. All electric motors are dependent upon it. Automobiles use it to start and to keep running. The sound coming from a radio is dependent upon it. The television picture is focused by it. The power that provides heat and light for our homes is generated by it. Many more uses could be listed, as electromagnets are working for us continually. See Photograph 15.

How an Electromagnet Is Made

When we made a permanent magnet with electromagnetism, we used hard

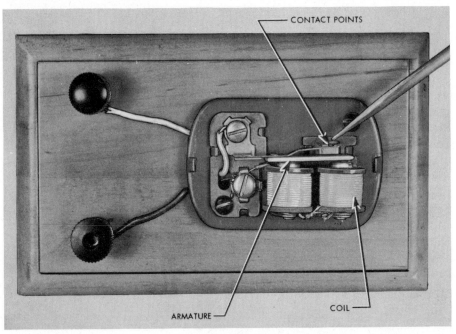

CONTACT POINTS

ARMATURE

COIL

◆ 15. The buzzer is an application of an electromagnet. Its vibrating motion is made through the use of a contact point. When the buzzer is connected to a source of electricity the coil attracts the armature. As soon as the armature is pulled toward the coil the points open and the coil loses its magnetism. The armature then returns to its original position where the points again make contact. At this time the electromagnet once more pulls the armature to the coil. The vibrating motion is the result of the electricity being continually turned off and on. The metal pointer in the photograph shows where the tone of the buzzer can be adjusted.

steel for the magnet. This was done because we wanted to retain the magnetism in the steel. Electromagnets are used in many electrical devices which require a very strong magnetic field and also require the magnetism to be started and stopped rapidly.

If we connect a coil of wire to a source of electricity, we will find that it will have a very weak attraction for iron. Now if we insert a piece of soft steel into the center of the coil, we will find that the electromagnet will lift a number of steel objects. This increase in magnetic strength is due to the soft steel core, which provides a better path for the magnetic field. Disconnecting the battery from the coil will cause the steel objects to drop from the core. This shows us that a soft steel core loses its magnetism easily. It also illustrates that when the coil is disconnected from the source of electricity, the electromagnet is no longer operating.

Basic Principles of Electromagnets

We have now stated the two principal requirements of an electromagnet: (1) It must have a strong magnetic field which can be concentrated through the use of a steel core. (2) It must have a soft steel core so that the magnetism can readily be controlled.

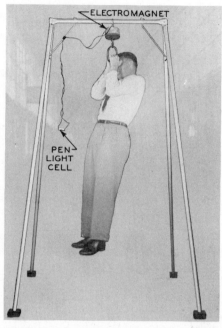

◆ 16. This is a small shop-made electromagnet that can lift several hundred pounds. A pen light cell was used as the source of electricity for the electromagnet to support a man weighing 180 pounds. Large commercial electromagnets are used to lift heavy steel objects weighing several tons.

The electromagnet can be made stronger or weaker, depending upon how strong the source of electricity is and upon the number of turns of wire around the core. We can increase the strength of the magnetic field if we can increase the power of the electric-

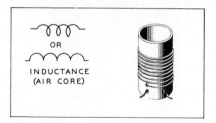

Both coil symbols are now in common use.

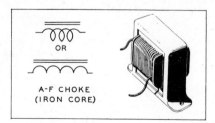

Two lines always indicate a magnetic core.

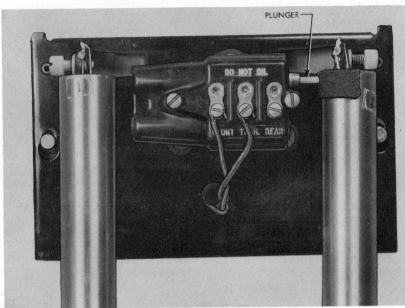

◆ 17. In a modern door chime a coil-and-plunger, often called a *solenoid,* is used for its operation. When the door button is pushed, the plunger is pulled into the coil against one of the chime tubes. As the button is released a spring pulls the plunger back out of the coil against the other chime tube. From this starting and stopping of the electricity we are able to get the two different tones from the chimes.

◆ 18. Model trains use the coil-and-plunger (solenoid) for moving the rail switch points. The two electromagnets are arranged so that one will pull the track in one direction and the other will push the track back in the other direction. Sometimes a common rail is used for the center connection of the two coils.

ity. Likewise, if the number of turns of wire around the core is increased, this too will increase the strength of the electromagnet. These two factors will be more fully explained in another section of this book.

Coil and Moving Plunger

Devices that require opening, closing, pushing, and pulling by remote

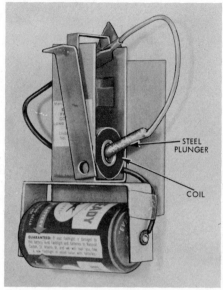

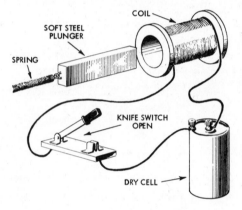

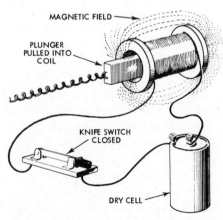

♦ 19. When the battery is connected to the coil, the plunger is magnetized and pulled into the center of the coil. When the battery is disconnected, the coil and plunger lose their magnetism and the spring pulls the plunger back.

♦ 20. A rear view of a coil-and-plunger used to provide motion in a commercial advertising sign. In operation the flashlight cell is connected to the coil of wire so that it pulls the steel core toward the center of the coil. As the plunger goes through the coil the battery is disconnected by the movement of the plunger. This permits the plunger to pass through the coil and after reaching the top of its swing it returns to the starting position. At this time the coil is reconnected to the dry cell and the plunger action starts over again. The device must be started by hand.

control usually use an electromagnet consisting of a coil and steel plunger, commonly called a *solenoid*. If we wind a coil of wire on a nonmagnetic hollow form, such as cardboard tubing, and connect it to a battery, it will set up a magnetic field around the coil. This field consists of lines of force that pass through the center of the coil. A small piece of soft steel placed near the hollow opening of the coil will be drawn into the coil, as shown in Illustration 19. This attraction, which causes the piece of steel to be pulled into the center of the coil, is due to the magnetism of the coil magnetizing the steel core. The molecules of the steel align themselves because they are attracted by the magnetic poles of the coil. We then have a coil acting like a magnet and magnetizing a steel core—the coil and the steel core attract each other. When the battery is disconnected, the coil loses its magnetism and, since it is made of soft steel, the plunger also loses its magnetism. This moving plunger can be used to push or pull various devices whenever the electricity is connected to the coil. If a spring is hooked onto the plunger, it will return the plunger to its original position as soon as the electricity is turned off. See Photograph 20.

INTERESTING THINGS TO DO

1. Making a Permanent Magnet by Means of Electricity.

Make a hollow tube by wrapping a piece of thin cardboard (tagboard) 2″ x 2″ around a ¼″ wood dowel. See Illustration 21. Using a fast drying glue, secure the overlapping cardboard. Be sure to avoid gluing the tubing to the dowel so that it can be removed easily. Out of heavy cardboard or ⅛″ masonite, shape two round washers about 1″ in diameter. Drill a hole in the center of each washer so that they can be fit snugly over the ends of the cardboard tubing. Drill a ¹⁄₁₆″ hole in one washer close to the center hole. A second ¹⁄₁₆″ hole should be drilled near the outside edge of the same washer. Glue one washer to each end of the tubing. Insert one end of a spool of No. 22 magnetic wire through the inner ¹⁄₁₆″ hole in the washer. Wind four, close-spaced, even layers of wire on the tubing and bring the end out through the outer hole in the washer. The two coil leads should be left about 6″ long.

Obtain a piece of hard steel ap-

◆ **21. Electromagnetic Coil**

proximately ¼″ x 3″. This can be a section of hacksaw blade, clock spring, or tool steel. Insert the steel into the center of the hollow coil. Connect the two ends of the coil to a dry cell for about ten seconds. Disconnect the cell and remove the hard steel core. Test the steel to see if it will attract small nails. What has happened to the steel? Hold one end of the steel near the north-seeking pole of a compass. Mark the polarity of your magnet.

2. Using a Plunger-Type Solenoid.

Obtain a piece of soft steel ¼″ in diameter and about 2½″ long. Insert the soft steel about halfway into the center of the coil made in Number 1. Connect one end of the coil to a dry cell, and momentarily make contact with the remaining coil lead to the other terminal of the cell. What happened to the soft steel core? Why did this occur? How can this principle be used on other electrical devices?

The coil that you have wound can be used on a number of different electrical projects such as a buzzer, door chime, motor, electrical lock, relay, or switch.

REVIEW QUESTIONS

1. What happens when a coil of wire is connected to a source of electricity?

2. When a piece of hard steel is placed in a coil connected to a source of electricity, what happens to the steel?

3. Give another name for *magnetic field*.

4. Make a list of some electrical devices that use electromagnets.

5. What effect does the steel core have on the magnetic field in an electromagnet?

6. Why isn't hard steel used in electromagnets?

7. What is a coil and moving plunger usually called?

8. Explain why a soft steel core will be pulled into the magnetic field of a coil.

How Electricity Is Produced

UNIT 6A
THE ELECTRON THEORY

Structure of Matter

Matter is anything that has weight and occupies space. It may be in the form of a solid, such as copper in an electrical conductor; a gas, such as hydrogen; or a liquid, such as water.

Using water as an example, let's analyze the structure of matter. If we took a drop of water and continued to divide it until it could not be divided further and still maintain the chemical properties of water, the smallest particle remaining would be a *molecule* of water.

Next, let's take this molecule of water and pass an electric current through it. This action will break down the molecule still further into its two component gases, hydrogen and oxygen. But these gases no longer have the properties of water. A substance that can be broken down into two or more basic parts, such as water,

is called a *compound*.

The hydrogen and oxygen which combined to make the water and which cannot be broken down further are known as *elements*. The smallest particle of an element which still has the chemical and electrical properties of that element is an *atom*. To make a molecule of water, two atoms of hydrogen and one atom of oxygen are needed. See Illustration 1A.

The Nature of Electricity

Before the acceptance of the electron theory, the effects of electricity could be seen, felt, and measured but could only be described as a mysterious force that traveled through a conductor at a speed of 186,000 miles per second. The electron theory is widely accepted today as an explanation of the flow of electricity through a conductor.

According to the electron theory, the atoms which make up all matter are

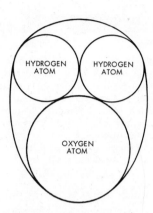

◆ 1A. Hydrogen and oxygen atoms unite to form a molecule of water.

composed of 3 types of particles, *protons, electrons,* and *neutrons.* The atoms of different materials vary only in the number and arrangement of these particles.

The electron is a particle of negative electrical charge revolving around the center of the atom, similar to the earth revolving around the sun. The center of the atom contains the positively charged particles called protons and the neutral particles (neutral in that they bear no charge) called neutrons. This center is termed the *nucleus* of the atom.

We have noted that there are two types of charged particles, positive and negative. Since the positive charge of the nucleus of the atom attracts the negative charge of the electron, we can say that *opposite charges attract.* In other words, there is a force of attraction between positive and negative charges.

When considering weight, we must note that the proton and neutron weigh about 1847 times as much as the electron. Thus the total weight of the proton and the neutron will determine the weight of the material.

For the sake of clarity, the structure of an atom is usually represented by a series of progressively larger orbits. But the paths of the electrons are generally thought of as following the inside circumference of spherical shells, one inside the other. The force which holds the electrons in their paths, preventing their breaking outward, is the attraction between the positively charged protons and the negatively charged electrons. The force which prevents the electrons from moving inward is centrifugal force, which is the force tending to make a rotating body move away from the center of rotation.

Except for the electrons in the outer shell, the particles of an atom are held tightly together and tremendous forces are required to pry them apart. Since the electrons in the outer shell are farthest from the nucleus, they are least attracted by the positive charge. In materials such as copper and silver which have only one electron in their outer shell, as shown in Illustration 1B, the electron may be easily dislodged. This characteristic makes these

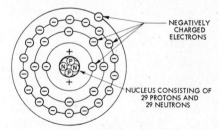

NEGATIVELY
CHARGED
ELECTRONS

NUCLEUS CONSISTING OF
29 PROTONS AND
29 NEUTRONS

◆ 1B. Arrangement of electrons in a copper atom.

materials very good electrical conductors.

Since the movement of electrons along a conductor corresponds to the flow of electricity, some means must be provided to start the electrons in motion. When an electrical circuit is connected to a source of supply, such as a dry cell, negatively charged electrons tend to flow from the negative terminal of the dry cell through the conductor. This movement dislodges a negatively charged electron from the outer shell of atom within the conductor and forces it to the next atom. The newly arrived electron forces the electron in the outer shell to the next atom where a similar action takes place in adjacent

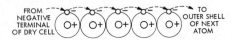

◆ **1C. When the negatively charged electron moves from the dry cell to atom A it forces the electron from the outer shell of atom A to atom B. The electron from atom B moves on to atom C where it displaces the outer electron and forces it to atom D. This movement continues on to atom E and through the remainder of the circuit to the positive terminal of the dry cell.**

atoms until the positive terminal of the dry cell is reached, as shown in Illustration 1C. While this step-by-step movement may seem like a slow process it is actually occurring at the speed of light, or approximately 186,-000 miles per second.

UNIT 6B

MAKING ELECTRICITY WITH CHEMICALS

A Simple Cell

Chemical action is one method of providing a source of electricity. Certain materials, usually metals and carbon, when placed in a liquid solution can produce electricity. A simple cell for producing electricity can be made by placing carbon and zinc in a solution of salammoniac. Salammoniac is used to clean soldering coppers and is available in powder or bar form. Salammoniac is known chemically as *ammonium chloride* and may be obtained in powder form at any drugstore. If the bar salammoniac is used it will be necessary to break off several small pieces and pound them into a

powder. The powder can then be mixed with the water in a glass.

A piece of zinc is placed in the glass with the salammoniac solution and a rod of carbon is put in so that it does not touch the zinc. A short length of insulated wire is then connected to the zinc and another wire to the carbon. The other ends of these wires are hooked to a 1½-volt flashlight bulb. The bulb will light, and the cell of zinc, carbon, and salammoniac is developing electricity. See Photograph 2.

Electrons

What makes our cell produce electricity? The solution of salammoniac and water, called an *electrolyte,* starts acting on the piece of zinc so that very small particles, not visible to the human eye, gather all around the zinc. These particles are called *electrons.* All electrons are considered to be negative particles of electricity. The electrons will pile up all around the zinc until there is not room for any more to get on it. The zinc which has all of the electrons around it is called the *negative pole.* A minus sign (−) is usually used to indicate the negative pole. See Illustration 3.

Since all of the electrons in the solution have gone to the zinc, the carbon is without electrons. We call this point where there is a shortage of electrons the *positive pole.* A plus sign (+) is usually used to indicate the positive pole. In electricity when we have a large number of electrons at one place they tend to try to move to a place where there is a shortage of electrons. The electrons in the electrolyte solution flow to the zinc. In order to allow the electrons on the zinc to reach the carbon an outside path must be provided.

Primary Cells

Cells which cannot be recharged are called *primary cells.* When we made

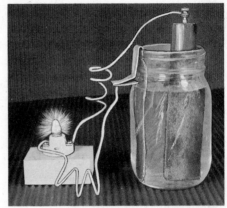

◆ 2. A simple cell made of zinc, carbon, and a solution of salammoniac. The three requirements for a complete electrical circuit are all connected together—a source of electricity, the cell; the two connecting wires; and the object that works from the electricity, the bulb.

the cell of zinc, carbon, and salammoniac it was a primary cell because it could not be recharged. The cell went "dead" because the zinc was dissolved in the electrolyte.

Direct Current

The flow of electrons from a cell through a circuit is called *direct current.* Direct current is a flow of electricity that is always in the same direction. A primary cell has one terminal that is negative (−) and the other that is positive (+). When the termi-

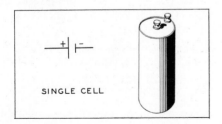

SINGLE CELL

Terminals of a cell are identified by the length of lines.

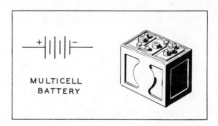

MULTICELL BATTERY

Cell symbols are combined to represent a battery.

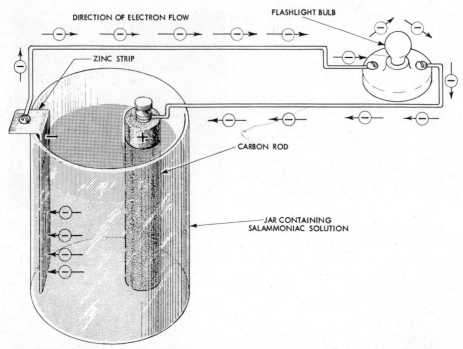

DIRECTION OF ELECTRON FLOW

FLASHLIGHT BULB

ZINC STRIP

CARBON ROD

JAR CONTAINING
SALAMMONIAC SOLUTION

◆ 3. The flashlight bulb is connected to the zinc and the carbon. The electrons start flowing from the zinc through the wire and the bulb so that they can get to the carbon. This flow of electrons is what is called a flow of electricity. The flow of electricity, then, is negative particles, called electrons, going from a point where there are many extra electrons to a point where there are very few.

nals were connected to a flashlight bulb, the electrons flowed from the negative terminal through the wire and bulb to the positive terminal. This is a direct current source of electricity because the electrons always travel in the same direction. The abbreviation for direct current is dc.

The Dry Cell

A primary cell that can be carried easily and handled without spilling the electrolyte is called a *dry cell*. See Illustration 4. These dry cells are used in flashlights, pen lights, radios, telephone circuits, and in many other places where direct current is needed. They differ mainly from the wet cell, which we have been discussing, in that the electrolyte is made of a paste instead of a liquid.

The dry primary cell will have about 1½ volts. See Photograph 5. As in the wet cell, the carbon is the positive (+) terminal and the zinc is the negative (−) terminal. The action is the same as in the wet cell. When the zinc is dissolved the cell goes dead.

Single dry cells are found in many shapes and sizes. Large cells are used where longer service is needed. Usually the larger the cell the longer it will last. Of course, when cells must be carried, as in flashlights, they are made small so that they are light in weight.

Batteries

When more than 1½ volts is needed, dry cells are connected so that the voltage of the cells can be added together. See Illustration 6. In a flashlight using two dry cells, the voltage produced by the two cells is 3 volts. When dry cells are placed together in one container and are connected to provide more voltage we call this a *battery*. These cells may be round in shape much as the pen light cell or can be made flat so that they will pack more compactly. Radio batteries are made to deliver various voltages, usually 1½, 6, 22½, 45, or 90 volts.

The Storage Cell

One of the disadvantages of the dry cell is that when it has been used for a period of time the cell becomes discharged and must be thrown away. A cell that can be used over and over again by recharging is called a *secondary cell*. This is the type of cell found in the storage battery that is used in automobiles. A storage cell that is being used as a source of electricity will run down, but after recharging it is ready for use again.

In the simple primary cell we used two unlike materials such as zinc and carbon in an electrolyte solution. The most common type of secondary cell is called a *lead-acid cell* since it contains plates of lead for both the positive and the negative terminals, and

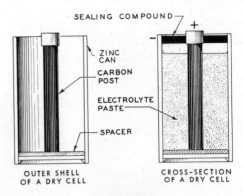

SEALING COMPOUND

ZINC CAN

CARBON POST

ELECTROLYTE PASTE

SPACER

OUTER SHELL OF A DRY CELL

CROSS-SECTION OF A DRY CELL

EXTERIOR VIEW OF A DRY CELL

◆ 4. If we examined a flashlight cell we would find that the outside is covered with cardboard but that the container is a zinc can. The center post is a carbon rod held in place at the top by an insulating material. Under the insulating top and in the zinc container can be found the electrolyte, which is sal-ammoniac in paste form with black manganese dioxide added.

sulfuric acid and distilled water for the electrolyte. We can construct a simple storage cell by putting a dilute solution of sulfuric acid in a glass container. Extreme care must be used in handling sulfuric acid as it is very dangerous. If the acid comes in contact with any part of the body it will burn the skin, and it will also burn holes in clothing. The acid should be diluted by first pouring the water into

◆ 5. This experiment demonstrates that regardless of the size a single dry cell will produce only 1½ volts.

the glass and then adding the acid very slowly. Two strips of lead are next placed in the acid solution so that they do not touch each other. These metal strips are both alike and the cell will not produce electricity until we can do something to change one of the pieces of lead.

◆ 6. Interior construction of a radio B battery showing how dry cells are connected together.

The cell needs to be *charged;* this can be done by using a source of direct current electricity such as that found in two dry cells. The dry cells should be connected so that they can pro duce 3 volts, the positive terminal being connected to one strip of lead and the negative terminal to the other strip. We can now notice that some action is taking place in the electrolyte as bubbles will start to appear in the solution. As the charging process continues, the lead plate connected to the positive terminal of our dry cell will start to turn brown. The negative plate will show little change in color. After about ten minutes we can disconnect our dry cells and test the storage cell to see if it can produce electricity.

Charging and Discharging a Storage Cell

When the cell has run down we can recharge it and use it again. During the charging process, two changes occurred in the cell. The plates became different in color, with the positive plate turning brown. The brown coating on the positive plate is chemically called *lead peroxide*. This charging has made the two lead plates different, one of the requirements of a primary cell. The electrolyte solution changes from a weak solution of sulfuric acid to a stronger solution of the acid. The change in the metals and the formation of stronger acid always occur during charging. The voltage of the fully charged cell is about 2 volts.

◆ 7A. Testing of a charged storage cell by connecting the two lead plate terminals to a flashlight bulb. The cell will soon run down if left connected to the bulb.

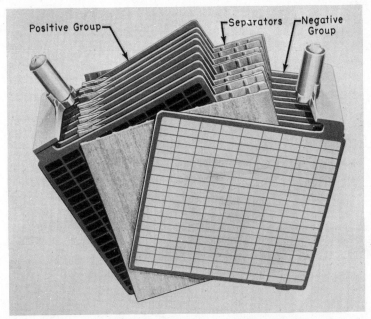

◆ 7B. Each cell of a commercial battery is made up of several negative plates and several positive plates held apart from the others, by insulated separators. These separators may be made of such insulating materials as wood, fiber glass, or rubber, and they keep the negative plates from touching the positive plates. In the cell all of the negative plates are connected together and all of the positive plates are connected together so that the cell will be able to handle heavy demands for electricity. The plates are made of a lead grid framework. The negative grids are filled with spongy lead and the positive plates are filled with lead peroxide.

Commercial Storage Batteries

Besides the advantage of recharging, the storage cell is much better than the dry cell where continuous heavy use is required. In automobiles the storage battery is used to start the engine, to provide power for the ignition circuit, and as a source of electricity for lights and accessories. Since more than 2 volts are usually necessary for these purposes, the battery is made of six lead-acid cells connected together to provide 12 volts. In some automobiles a 6-volt storage battery is used.

Testing a Storage Battery

One method of testing a storage battery is to test the acid in each of the cells by means of a *hydrometer*.

The hydrometer contains a float inside of a glass tube. The float will rise with liquids heavier than water. A term, *specific gravity,* is applied when comparing the weight of different liquids with that of water. Water is given a value of 1.000 in weight, which is called its specific gravity. See Illustration 9.

When a battery has been in use for some time the electrolyte becomes lower in the cells. This is due to evaporation. Pure water, called *distilled water,* must be used to refill the cell. After a battery has been in service for a long time it will lose its capacity for being recharged. This is because the paste becomes loose in the grids of the plates, and the plates start to buckle. At this time the battery must either be rebuilt or replaced by a new one.

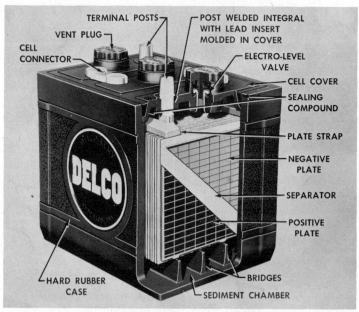

◆ 8. **The illustration shows the interior construction of a typical 6-volt automobile battery.**

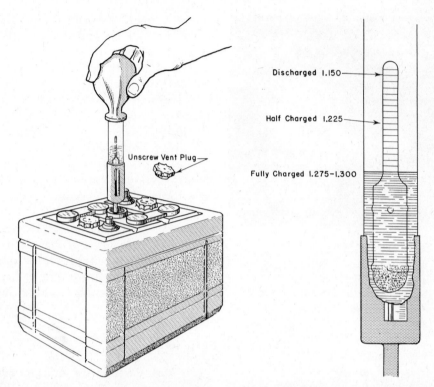

Unscrew Vent Plug

Discharged 1.150

Half Charged 1.225

Fully Charged 1.275–1.300

◆ 9. When sulfuric acid from a fully charged cell is drawn into a hydrometer it will read about 1.300, as the acid is heavier than water. This heavy acid made the float stay up higher in the liquid than it would with water. When a battery is discharged, part of the acid has returned to the plates. The solution in the cell now has less acid than before and the specific gravity will read about 1.150.

INTERESTING THINGS TO DO

1. Making a Simple Wet Cell.

In a pint glass jar mix a solution of water and salammoniac. Keep adding powdered salammoniac to the water and stir the solution until no more salammoniac will dissolve. Obtain an old dry cell and remove the center carbon rod. Cut a strip of zinc about 1″ wide and 6″ long. Place both the zinc and the carbon in the solution so that they do not touch each other. Connect a wire to the carbon and an-other wire to the zinc strip. Attach the other ends of the wires to a 1½-volt flashlight bulb. Why does the bulb light? What is happening in the cell?

2. Making a Simple Storage Cell.

Pour a dilute solution of sulfuric acid into a pint glass jar. USE EXTREME CARE IN HANDLING THE ACID. If the acid needs to be diluted, be sure to put the water into the jar first and add the acid slowly. Obtain two lead

◆ **10. A Simple Storage Cell**

strips approximately 1″ x 6″. Place these two strips in the electrolyte solution so that they do not touch each other. Connect one wire to one lead strip and another wire to the other strip. Two dry cells should be connected so that they produce 3 volts. To do this connect the negative terminal of one cell to the positive terminal of the other cell. One wire from the lead strips goes to the remaining negative terminal of the two cells and the other wire goes to the remaining positive terminal. The storage cell is now being charged. Notice what is happening to the lead plates. Let the charging action continue for about ten minutes. In place of the two dry cells, connect the wires from the storage cell to a flashlight bulb or a buzzer. What is happening? Why do we call this a *secondary cell?*

REVIEW QUESTIONS

1. Define an atom.

2. What holds the electrons in their paths as they rotate around the nucleus?

3. Why are silver and copper good electrical conductors?

4. At what speed does an electron move from atom to atom in a conductor?

5. What are the three requirements for a complete circuit?

6. Explain the difference between a wet and a dry cell.

7. What is the difference between a primary and a secondary cell?

8. What is meant by *electron flow?*

9. In a primary cell what happens when the cell goes dead?

10. Explain what we mean when we say that a direct current is flowing.

11. How does the size of a dry cell affect its operation?

12. What happens when a storage cell is being charged?

13. State the purpose of the separators in a commercial storage battery.

14. How can you determine the charge of a storage cell?

15. Why do commercial storage batteries have more than one plate for each cell?

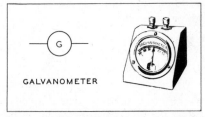

GALVANOMETER

Letter symbols in a circle are used to identify any instrument.

UNIT 7
GENERATING ELECTRICITY WITH MAGNETISM

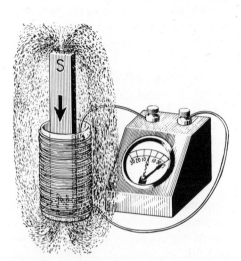

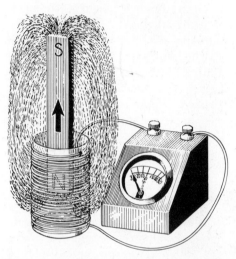

◆ 11. The galvanometer is connected to the two ends of the coil. Holding the bar magnet in one hand, we should then push it through the center of the coil of wire. Immediately we will notice that the needle of the galvanometer moved in one direction and then comes back to zero in the center of the dial.

◆ 12. When we pull the magnet back out of the coil the meter needle moves in the opposite direction and then comes back to zero.

Batteries are very useful for providing a source of electricity but they are limited in the amount of electricity that they can produce. To produce great quantities of electricity, a method of making it by means of a magnetic field is generally used. The generators and dynamos found in electric plants throughout the world use the principle of electromagnetism to make electricity.

Moving Bar Magnet

To produce electricity by a magnetic field we need a coil of wire and a magnet. A coil can be wound of about 25 turns of wire around a 1″

hollow tubing. To indicate that electricity is being produced we need a very sensitive instrument called a *galvanometer*. A galvanometer is used to show that a very small quantity of electrons is flowing in a circuit. Usually the pointer or needle of the meter points to the center of the dial when not in use. When electricity flows through the meter, the needle will move either to the left or right.

Each time we push the magnet toward the center of the coil the galvanometer needle will move in one direction, and each time we pull the magnet out, the needle will move in the other direction. If we leave the magnet inside of the coil the galvanometer needle does not move. To produce electricity, as shown by the galvanometer, we need to have the magnet moving in or out of the coil. See Illustrations 11 and 12.

Turn the bar magnet around so that the other pole is pushed into the coil first. Now we will notice that the needle moves in the opposite direction. This shows us that the direction of the galvanometer needle movement depends upon which direction the magnet is pushed or pulled. The direction that electricity flows depends upon which direction the bar magnet is moving.

Moving Coil

If we hold the bar magnet steady in one hand and place the coil so that the hollow center can be moved back and forth over the magnet we will again notice the galvanometer needle moves first in one direction and then in the other. The coil can be turned over so that the opposite end starts moving over the magnet first. Now the needle will move in the opposite direction. From this we can see that electricity can be produced either by moving a magnet in a coil or wire or by having a coil of wire move over a magnet.

Induced Electricity

Why did the coil and bar magnet produce electricity? When we studied magnetism in Unit 4 we found that a magnet always had a magnetic field around it. When either the magnet is moving or the coil is moving, the wires in the coil are cutting through the magnetic field of the magnet. Cut-

ting through the magnetic field by the coil produces what is called *induced* electricity. Electricity can be induced in the coil only when either the magnet or the coil is in motion.

Alternating Current

The bar magnet, when pushed in or out of the coil, made the galvanometer needle move first in one direction and then in the other. This was due to the cutting of the magnetic field which induced electricity in the coil. This induced electricity is a flow of electrons through the coil and galvanometer. When the bar magnet was pushed into the center of the coil, the electrons began to flow in one direction. As soon as the magnet was stopped, the electrons stopped flowing in the circuit. Electrons started to flow again in the opposite direction when the magnet was pulled out of the coil. The flow of electrons, first in one direction, then stopping and starting to flow again in the opposite direction, is called *alternating current*. This is different from direct current, which always flows in the same direction.

Alternating current electricity, which is abbreviated ac, always flows first one way through the circuit and

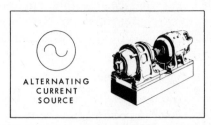

ALTERNATING
CURRENT
SOURCE

This symbol is used to indicate any source of alternating current.

then reverses and starts flowing in the other direction. We later shall find that there are many reasons why alternating current is used.

Frequency

The faster that we move the bar magnet in and out of the coil the faster the electrons must change direction of flow through the coil and galvanometer. The electron flow changes direction every time the magnet changes direction. We say that the electrons have completed one *cycle* of flow when the magnet has been pushed into and pulled out of the coil once. One cycle of electricity might be compared to an automobile engine that turns over once. The engine in making one revolution has completed one cycle of its motion before it starts the second revolution. To make a second cycle of alternating current we must plunge the magnet in and out of the coil again. Each time we do this we complete one cycle of alternating current.

The number of cycles completed in one second is called the *frequency*. We can develop a frequency of 10 cycles per second alternating current by pushing the magnet in and out of the coil ten times every second.

The frequency of alternating current coming into most homes is 60 cycle. This means that the alternating current is changing direction 120 times every second.

A Simple Generator

If a coil of wire is moved in a mag-

netic field we know that the cutting of the lines of magnetic force will produce electricity. This is the principle of the *generator,* which is used to produce most of the electricity that we use. A generator has a moving coil that can be rotated in a magnetic field. The rotating coil is usually called an *armature.* The magnetic field can be made of two magnetic poles such as found in a horseshoe magnet. See Illustration 13.

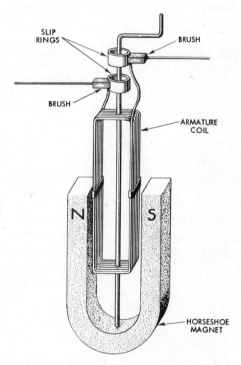

◆ 13. To obtain electricity from the rotating coil we must be able to connect onto the two ends of the coil. This requires the construction of special devices called slip rings or a commutator. The contact to the slip rings or commutator is made by two brushes. The drawing shows how the brushes are always in contact with the two ends of the coil through the use of slip rings.

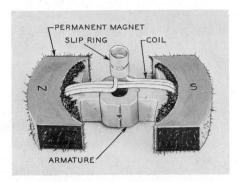

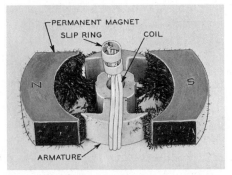

◆ 14. A photograph of the basic parts necessary in a simple alternating current generator. The iron filings have been sprinkled on the magnets and form a pattern representing the magnetic field. Notice that the coil is cutting through the maximum number of lines of force when it is directly opposite the two poles of the magnet. The greatest amount of electricity is produced at this time.

◆ 15. In this photograph the coil has been rotated one-quarter of a turn and now it is not cutting any of the lines of force. Electricity is not being produced at this part of the rotation of the armature.

Alternating Current Generator

To make contact with the coil as it rotates, two separate rings are placed

around the shaft of the armature. One ring is connected to one end of the coil and the other ring to the other end of the coil. The rings must not touch each other and must not touch the armature shaft except through an

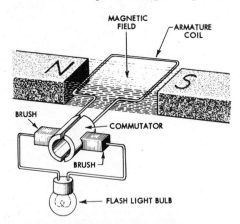

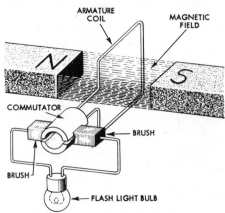

◆ 16. A drawing of a simple direct current generator. The armature is now cutting the maximum number of lines of force. One brush is always in contact with the side of the coil going up on the left side of the armature. The other brush is in contact with the side of the coil going down on the right side.

◆ 17. As the armature rotates a quarter of a turn, the coil is cutting a minimum number of lines of force. At the same time the coil, through the commutator, changes connection with the brushes. This produces direct current electricity.

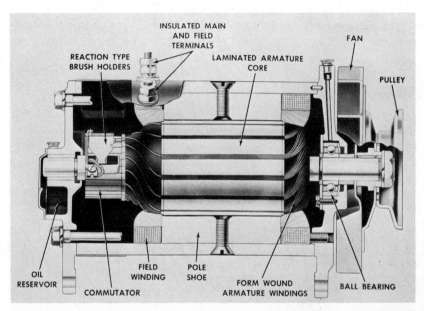

Courtesy Delco-Remy Div.—General Motors Corp.

◆ 18. Automobile generators usually have a number of coils on the armature. The end of each coil comes out to a separate section of the commutator. These sections are insulated from each other and are called *segments*. The segments are connected to the coils so that each can deliver its electricity to the brushes.

Most automobile generators use an electromagnet for the magnetic field. The electromagnet provides a strong magnetic field for the armature. The coils used to produce the electromagnetism are called *field coils*. These field coils receive their electricity from the armature.

insulating material. These two rings are called *slip rings* (Photographs 14 and 19). As they rotate two *brushes* made either of soft copper or carbon are always in contact with the rings.

When the coil rotates in the magnetic field, made by the two poles of the magnet, the greatest amount of electricity is produced in the coil when it is cutting the largest number of lines of force. The coil is cutting the largest number of lines of force when it is moving directly across the ends of the two poles. See Photograph 14.

The coil cuts the fewest lines of force when each part of the coil is moving farthest away from the center of the magnetic field. The amount of electricity produced in the coil is large when the coil is moving between the two magnets. No electricity is produced when the coils are cutting none of the lines of force. See Photograph 15.

When a coil was moved in and out of a magnet, we said an alternating current was being produced because it would cut the magnetic field first in one direction and then in the other direction. This same action takes place

◆ 19. A photograph of an experimental alternating current generator. The commutator is used to develop direct current for the field coils. Alternating current is obtained from the brush posts connected to the slip rings.

as the coil rotates between the two poles of the magnet. The induced electricity flows out through the brushes first one way and then the other, as the coil is rotated in the magnetic field. The alternating current is not constant and is changing in amount depending upon where the coil is in the magnetic field.

Direct Current Generators

To obtain direct current from a generator we use a *commutator* instead of slip rings. The commutator (Illustrations 16 and 19) consists of a single ring cut in two so that each half is separated from the other on the armature shaft. One side of the commutator is connected to one end of the coil and the other side to the other end of the coil. Brushes make continuous contact with the commutator to pick up the electron flow from the coil. During each half rotation of the armature, the brushes make contact with a different end of the coil. See Illustration 17.

Thus through the use of a commu-

ROTATING
PERMANENT MAGNET
FIELD

STATIONARY
ARMATURE
COIL

◆ 20. This photograph shows how alternating current can be developed with stationary armature coils and a rotating permanent magnet field. As the magnet rotates it induces an alternating current in the stationary coils. Slip rings are not necessary on this generator. Generators used on bicycles are of this type.

tator we are able to get direct current from the generator. This direct current is varying in strength the same as the alternating current. The difference is in the electron flow, which is always in the same direction for direct current. We call this changing in strength of direct current *pulsating* direct current.

Commercial Generators

One of the requirements for all generators is that we have some means of power to rotate them. The army uses hand power to turn over some

Courtesy Westinghouse Electric Corp.

◆ 21. Modern railroads use electric power to drive their trains. This train uses a diesel engine to operate a large electric generator. The generator is then used to provide electricity for an electric motor that moves the train.

◆ 22. Modern electric power generators are streamlined and compact. This steam-driven generator is capable of supplying electricity to a city of 225,000 people.

of their portable field generators. Large generators are run by water turbines, or by gasoline, steam, or diesel engines.

Most generators built commercially have more than one set of coils in the armature. By having more coils in the armature it is possible to produce a more constant supply of electricity. This is because some of the coils are always directly across from the poles of the magnet. It is at this point that the greatest amount of electricity is induced in the coil.

The automobile generator (Illustration 18) uses a commutator to produce direct current electricity. Since the brushes deliver direct current to the field coils each pole always has the same north and south polarity. This type of generator is used for direct current arc welding and many other places where direct current is needed.

Most alternating current generators also use electromagnetic field coils instead of permanent magnets. The magnetic field must always have the same poles and the same polarity. This is not possible with alternating current electricity because the electrons are flowing first in one direction and then the other. We can see that if the field coils were connected to the slip rings of the alternating current generator the poles in the field would always be changing. Alternating current generators, like direct current generators, must have constant north and south poles for the electromagnetic field. Some method must be used in alternating current generators to supply direct current to the field coils. This can be done by having a separate generator to produce the direct current. Another method is to have two generators connected together on one armature.

INTERESTING THINGS TO DO

Making and Using a Galvanometer.
Use the small compass constructed in Unit 4. The wooden base should be approximately 1½" square. Cut two pieces of heavy cardboard the same length as the base and wide enough so that the top of the cardboard will be approximately ⅛" above the top of the compass needle. Glue the two pieces of cardboard on the sides of the base as shown in Illustration 23. Wind about 40 turns of No. 28 magnet wire around the compass. In order to be able to see the compass it is best to wind 20 turns on one side of the needle and the other 20 turns on the other side as shown in the picture. This completes the construction of the galvanometer.

Obtain a piece of cardboard tubing about 1" in diameter and 2½" long. Wind approximately 100 turns of No.

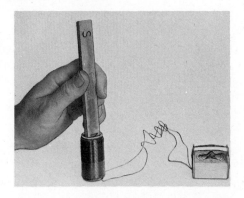

◆ **23. Shop Constructed Galvanometer Indicating Electron Flow**

22 wire on the form. Connect the two ends of the coil to the two leads on the galvanometer. Keep the coil and galvanometer about 18" apart. Push a bar magnet into the coil. Now move the magnet back and forth through the coil. What happens to the compass needle? Why?

REVIEW QUESTIONS

1. What is the purpose of a galvanometer?

2. How does reversing the poles of the bar magnet affect the movement of the galvanometer?

3. Why does a coil with a moving bar magnet produce electricity?

4. When alternating current is produced, in what direction do the electrons flow?

5. How does alternating current differ from direct current?

6. What is the number of cycles completed by an alternating current in just one second properly called?

7. In 60-cycle alternating current how many cycles are completed in one minute?

8. What is the difference between commutators and slip rings on generators?

9. When a generator is rotating, at what position is the largest quantity of electricity produced?

10. List the different types of power used to turn generators.

11. In automobile generators how is the magnetic field obtained?

UNIT 8

PRODUCING ELECTRICITY WITH FRICTION, HEAT, LIGHT, AND PRESSURE

Static Electricity

Probably everyone has had the experience of receiving a shock from touching the door of an automobile just as he started to get out of the car. Possibly you have received a shock when you walked on a heavy rug and then touched another person. These shocks were caused by *static electricity.*

When riding in an automobile your body moves against the seat and back cushions. Rubbing against the cushions gives your body a charge of static electricity. When you touch the door of the automobile, this charge jumps to the door and you feel a shock. The charge was neutralized by the metal of the door. The same is true when you walk across a rug; the friction of your shoes against the rug produces a charge on your body. When you touch someone, the charge is neutralized by the other person.

Static electricity is made by friction which is the result of two different nonmetal materials, called *insulators,* rubbing against one another. Most insulating materials are what we call *neutral.* They have an equal number of negative and positive charges. If we rub two different materials together, one will rub some of the electrons off the other. The material which has gathered electrons onto it is said to have a negative charge, and the one that has lost electrons is said to have a

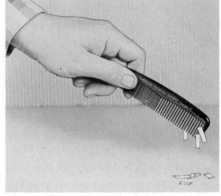

◆ 24. An example of static electricity can be shown by rubbing a comb against a piece of wool clothing. The comb becomes charged as the electrons are rubbed onto it from the wool. When the comb is touched against a small scrap of paper, it will attract the paper and pick it up. The comb, which has a negative charge, repels all of the electrons on the edge of the paper nearest to the comb. The electrons on the paper next to the comb go to the opposite end of the paper. The negative comb now attracts the positively charged edge.

positive charge. As the electrons jump from one point to another we see a spark and feel a shock.

Charges of static electricity can be compared with magnetism. In magnetism unlike poles attract and like poles repel. The same principle is true in static electricity: *Unlike charges attract each other and like charges repel each other.* See Illustrations 25 and 26.

Problems Caused by Static Electricity

Static electricity in many instances

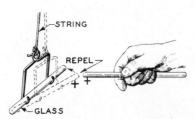

◆ 25. Both glass rods have been rubbed with a piece of silk. The silk rubs the electrons off of the glass, making them positively charged. Since both glass rods have a positive charge they will repel each other.

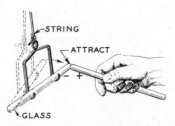

◆ 26. The glass rod hanging from the string has been rubbed with a piece of fur. The glass takes electrons off the fur, giving it a negative charge. The other glass rod was rubbed with silk, giving it a positive charge. The two unlike charged glass rods will attract each other.

is destructive and we need to find ways to control it. Trucks carrying gasoline become charged from the gasoline sloshing around in the tank and from the friction of the tires on the highway. This static charge could result in a spark which might ignite the gasoline. As a result all gasoline trucks have a chain or tape dragging on the ground to prevent the charge from developing. Rotating belts used on machinery can develop a static charge. When these belts are used around explosives it is necessary to ground the parts making contact with the belts. This grounding prevents the charge from developing, and thus prevents a spark that might cause an explosion.

Uses for Static Electricity

Some very important uses have been found for static electricity. Probably the most well known is the flue precipitator (Illustration 28) which is used in removing dust and smoke from the air. Clothing brushes with plastic bristles pick up the lint from

clothing because the plastic bristles become charged with electricity due to the friction caused by rubbing them against clothing.

Courtesy General Electric Co.

◆ 27. Static electricity is responsible for lightning. The friction caused by the small droplets in the clouds gives the clouds a charge of static electricity. When the charge becomes strong enough in the cloud, it discharges to the earth. This discharge of static electricity from the cloud to the earth results in a huge flash and a loud noise.

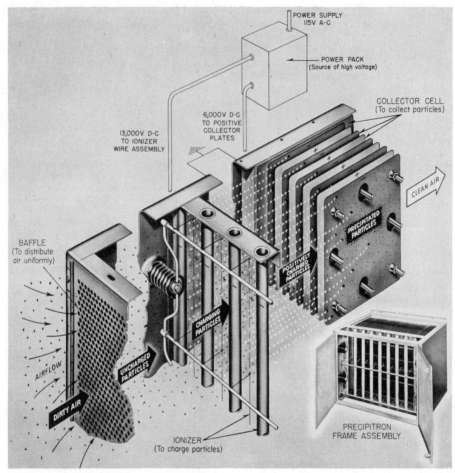

POWER SUPPLY
115V A-C

POWER PACK
(Source of high voltage)

COLLECTOR CELL
(To collect particles)

6,000V D-C
TO POSITIVE
COLLECTOR
PLATES

13,000V D-C
TO IONIZER
WIRE ASSEMBLY

CLEAN AIR

BAFFLE
(To distribute
air uniformly)

PRECIPITATED
PARTICLES

POSITIVELY
CHARGED
PARTICLES

CHARGING
PARTICLES

UNCHARGED
PARTICLES

AIRFLOW

DIRTY AIR

PRECIPITRON
FRAME ASSEMBLY

IONIZER
(To charge particles)

Courtesy Westinghouse Electric Corp.

◆ **28.** The precipitator is used as an air cleaner. It consists of one set of plates that have a high negative charge and another set of plates that have a high positive charge. The dust or smoke is first given a negative charge as it passes by the negatively charged plates. These particles then flow past a set of plates that have a positive charge. The negatively charged particles are attracted to the positive plates.

Sanding belts are sometimes coated by static electricity. The abrasive is charged by placing the grains in a very strong static electricity field. This charging makes the grains of the abrasive stand on end as iron filings stand in a magnetic field. While the grains are held on end, they are glued onto the belt. The end grains make a much sharper edge for sanding.

The Thermocouple

Heat can be used to develop very small amounts of electricity. If we twist a piece of constantan wire and a piece of iron wire together and heat them where they are joined together, a small quantity of electricity will be developed. See Photograph 29. We can indicate that electricity is being produced if we connect a galvanometer to the ends of the two pieces of wire. The producing of electricity by heating two different kinds of metal is called the *thermocouple* method.

The thermocouple method of making electricity is used to measure high temperatures. Two different metals such as platinum and iridium are joined together and are placed in a

◆ 29. A match will provide enough heat to generate electricity from a thermocouple.

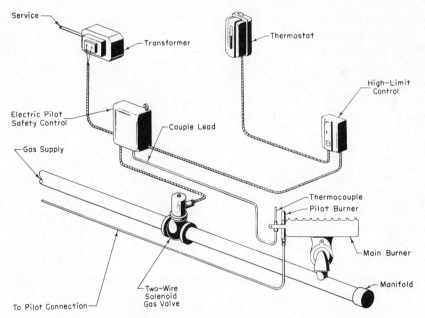

◆ 30. One use for a thermocouple is to automatically control a gas furnace so as to maintain an even temperature at all times.

heating unit. The electricity developed by the heating of the two different metals is shown by a galvanometer. As the temperature is increased the voltage produced by the thermocouple increases. This increased electricity makes the galvanometer needle move farther on the scale. The scale on the galvanometer is marked to read degrees of temperature. Thus by reading the scale of the meter, we can tell the amount of heat being produced. This type of meter is called a *pyrometer*.

Automatic gas furnaces sometimes use thermocouple electricity to open and close the supply valve. The pilot light of the furnace heats the two different metals to produce the electricity. When the wall thermometer, called a *thermostat*, closes the circuit due to changing of the room temperature, the thermocouple (Illustration 30) develops electricity to operate a coil and steel plunger device called a *solenoid*. This solenoid opens the gas valve. As soon as the room reaches the correct temperature the wall thermostat opens the circuit and the solenoid shuts the gas off.

The Photoelectric Tube

Certain materials such as potassium, sodium, and caesium when held in the light will give off small quantities of electrons. These materials, called *photosensitive*, are used in *photoelectric* cells. A photoelectric tube (Illustration 31) consists of a curved plate coated with the photosensitive material. A rod of metal is placed near the curved plate. Both the rod (*anode*) and plate (*cathode*) are sealed inside of a glass

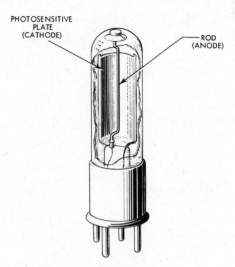

PHOTOSENSITIVE PLATE (CATHODE)

ROD (ANODE)

◆ 31. Photoelectric cells can be used for many purposes.

tube. When light shines on the curved plate it gives off electrons. We know that electrons are negative particles of electricity and that they will go to a place that has a positive charge. By connecting the rod to the positive side of a battery it will attract the electrons given off by the plate. The brighter the light that shines on it, the more electrons it will give off.

The ability of light to produce a flow of electrons in a photoelectric tube is used for many purposes. In almost all cases the photo tube must be used with some type of amplifier to make the small flow of electrons strong enough to do work. Doors are opened by having a light shine on a photoelectric tube. When someone walks between the light and the photoelectric tube the electrons are stopped momentarily. The amplifier circuit is so arranged that when the electrons stop it will turn on the motor that

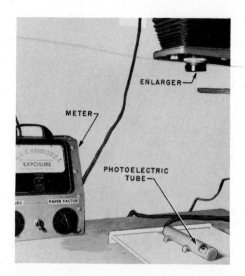

♦ 33. A simple Light Meter

♦ 32. A shop constructed exposure meter using a photoelectric tube to make photographic enlargements. The photo tube picks up light from the photographic enlarger. This photo tube is connected to the meter so that the amount of light on the tube will be recorded on the meter. The meter is calibrated to indicate the length of time in seconds necessary for each enlargement.

opens the door. Burglar alarms, lights, and many types of machines are controlled by photo tubes. One very common use for the photo tube is in the light meter used to measure the amount of light shining on a particular place. See Photograph 32.

The Selenium Cell

To develop power through the use of sunlight has been the goal of many inventors. The use of selenium makes this goal attainable. Selenium is another material that will give off electrons when light shines on it. Selenium is used in the new type of cell called a "sun battery" (Photograph 33). When

artificial light or sunlight shines on the selenium surface of the cell a small voltage is generated by the cell. Several of these cells may be connected together to produce increased amounts of electricity. Many uses can be made of this cell wherever artificial light or sunlight is available. Light measurement, automatic light control, light beam communication, timing devices, and many other commercial applications are possible with the sun battery.

Pressure Produces Electricity

Very small quantities of electricity can be produced when pressure is applied to some kinds of crystals. These crystals, such as quartz or Rochelle salts, will generate electricity when they are squeezed between two metal plates; and if a very sensitive meter is connected across the plates, voltage will be indicated. The greater the pressure that is placed on the crystals, the greater the resulting voltage. This ability to generate electricity by compressing a crystal is known as the *piezoelectric effect* of crystals.

Crystal Phonograph Pick Up

A good example of the piezoelectric effect is found in crystal phonograph pick-up arms. These pick-up arms use a crystal such as Rochelle salts with a needle attached as shown in Figure 34. As the needle rides in the grooves of the phonograph record, it is vibrated back and forth by small variations that are found in the record grooves. These variations are due to the sound vibrations that were impressed in the record when it was manufactured. Since the needle is connected to the crystal, the vibrations picked up by the needle are applied to the crystal. Thus, a varying pressure is placed on the crystal. This variation in pressure produces a weak voltage change which is then sent to a phonograph amplifier. The phonograph amplifier increases the varying voltage produced by the crystal and the electrical impulses are then converted back into sound waves by the loud speaker.

The Crystal Microphone

Another method of using crystals to generate electricity is found in the crystal microphone, often used in broadcasting stations or public address systems.

When someone speaks into a crystal microphone, the sound waves strike the

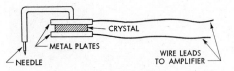

◆ 34. A sketch of a crystal phonograph pick-up. As the needle vibrates in the record grooves, these vibrations are delivered to the metal plates next to the crystal. These vibrations press on the crystal and a voltage variation is then produced by the crystal between the two metal plates. The varying voltage is then fed into an amplifier.

crystal in the microphone and compress it. The sound waves are converted into a weak electric current by the crystal. This small current is then fed into an amplifier where the signal is made strong enough to operate a loud speaker.

Crystal Vibration

Another piezoelectric effect of a crystal is its ability to vibrate or produce mechanical motion. When a voltage is applied across a pair of plates that have been placed on opposite sides of a crystal, a vibration will be set up by the crystal. The number of vibrations per second that will be produced by the crystal is very constant. These vibrations are called the frequency of the crystal, which is basically determined by the type of crystal and its thickness. Such crystals are usually cut from quartz and are used in broadcasting stations, for example, where fixed frequencies are very important.

INTERESTING THINGS TO DO

1. Generating Static Electricity.
Cut several small pieces of scrap paper and place them on a flat wooden surface. Charge a comb by rubbing it

on woolen clothing. Hold the comb near the scrap pieces of paper. What happens? Why?

2. Making a Thermocouple.

Cut a piece of constantan wire 6" long and a piece of iron wire the same length. Wire sizes between No. 14 and No. 20 will be satisfactory. Twist the two wires together for a distance of about 1½". Connect the opposite ends of the wire to a very sensitive galvanometer or a low reading milliammeter, an instrument that measures small currents. Heat the twisted ends of the wires with a match or a gas flame. Why does the needle on the meter move? Reverse the two wire connections to the meter. What happens?

3. Making a Simple Light Meter.

Obtain a selenium photo cell or a sun battery. Connect the two leads from the cell to a milliammeter (0-to-1 or 0-to-5 milliamperes). Be sure to connect the red or positive lead of the cell to the side of the meter marked "positive." Hold the face of the cell toward the window in your room. Observe the reading of the meter. Place the cell directly under a light bulb. How does the meter reading compare with the one taken from the window light? This meter may be constructed and calibrated for use as a light meter for photographic work.

REVIEW QUESTIONS

1. In what ways are static electricity and magnetism similar?

2. List some of the problems caused by static electricity.

3. Name several uses made of static electricity.

4. What are the requirements necessary to produce electricity by the thermocouple method?

5. Name several commercial uses of the thermocouple.

6. How does a photoelectric tube operate?

7. Why is it necessary to have an amplifier when using a photoelectric tube?

8. Make a list of purposes for which the photoelectric tube is used.

9. What is the principal material used in the sun battery?

10. Suggest a new type of use that might be made of the sun battery.

11. What is the material used to produce electricity by pressure?

12. Explain how pressure is used to produce electricity in a phonograph pick-up.

Basic

Electrical

Circuits

$I = E \times R$

UNIT 9
MEASURING THE VOLTAGE

Voltage and Pressure

We have said that the voltage of a dry cell is 1½ volts and that the voltage of a storage battery is 6 volts. You have probably heard that the electricity in your home is 115 volts. The various voltages indicate the amount of pressure that each of these sources produces.

Voltage is the pressure or force that

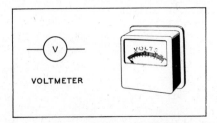

The letter "V" indicates a voltmeter symbol.

pushes electrons through an electrical circuit. A single cell of a storage battery produces a pressure of 2 volts. When three cells are connected together they produce three times as much pressure as one cell. The voltage of the battery is 6 volts. The greater the pressure or voltage the more electrons will be forced to flow through a circuit.

Voltage might be compared to the water system in a city. Most towns have a large tank that is used to force water through pipes to the houses throughout the community. The water pressure is available whenever the faucet is opened. If the water in the tank gets low the pressure in the system is low.

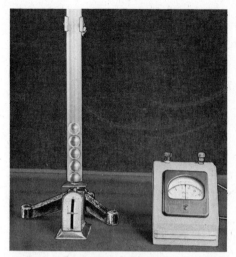

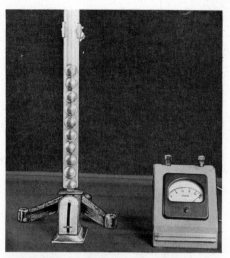

◆ 1A. In the photograph the five steel balls have been placed in a clear plastic tube so they are pushing down on the scale used for measuring weights. These balls are providing enough pressure to force the pointer of the weighing scale to the center of the dial. Electrical pressure may be compared to this. The voltmeter is showing electrical pressure forcing the needle to the center of the scale.

◆ 1B. This photograph shows the pointer of the weighing scale almost at the bottom of the dial, indicating that the weight has been increased. The addition of the five steel balls in the plastic tube has increased the pressure and the increase may be measured by the scale. The electrical pressure increased may be compared to this. The voltage was increased and the voltmeter shows this increase.

In electricity, the source of electricity produces the voltage the same as the water tank provides the pressure. The greater the voltage, the greater the force of the electricity. This force is called the *electromotive force* and is measured in *volts*.

Producing an Electromotive Force

The electromotive force, or voltage, may be produced by generators, dry cells, batteries, thermocouples, photoelectric cells, or sun batteries. Generators are the most common source of voltage and are used when large quantities of voltage are needed. Batteries are usually used where it is not convenient to use generators and where direct current is needed. The other methods of producing voltage have limited use except in special places where small quantities of voltage are needed.

COMMON VOLTAGES

Some very common voltages that can be obtained from various devices are listed below:

Thermocouple	Few thousandths of a volt
Dry cell	1½ volts
Storage battery	6 and 12 volts
Door chime transformer	12 to 24 volts
Home outlets	110 to 120 volts
Electric lines into homes	110–220 to 120–240 volts
Transformers on power poles	2,400 to 4,200 volts
Power company substation	12,000 to 69,000 volts
Power company generators	12,500 volts
Long distance transmission lines	287,000 volts

Using Voltmeters

A voltmeter is used to measure electromotive force. The meter is connected directly across the two terminals where the voltage is to be measured. One connection of the meter goes to one wire of the circuit and the other connection to the other wire as in Illustration 2.

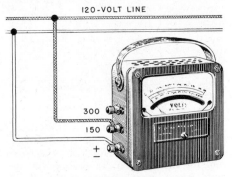

◆ **2. When measuring the voltage of a power line, one terminal of the voltmeter is connected to one side of the line and the other terminal of the meter to the other side of the line.**

When selecting a voltmeter it is necessary to know whether the electricity is alternating current or direct current. Direct current meters will not read alternating current voltages and alternating current meters will give incorrect readings of direct current.

It is also important that the meter

◆ **3. This is a drawing of one type of meter scale. Each meter scale has division markings which make it possible to read the meter accurately. The divisions found on the scale vary with the type of meter used.**

◆ **4. Measuring the voltage of a storage battery with a meter having a 0-to-25—volt scale.**

◆ **5. A wiring diagram of Photograph 4. Wiring diagrams, sometimes called *schematic diagrams*, use electrical symbols to show how the parts are connected.**

used have the correct scale for the voltage to be measured. If the voltage is too high for the meter it will burn out the meter.

To measure the voltage of a storage battery that delivers 6 volts, a direct current meter that has a full scale reading of 10 volts is generally used. If the meter had a 0-to-200—volt scale, the 6 volts of the storage battery would move the needle so slightly that it would be difficult to obtain an accurate reading. A meter that had a 0-to-1—volt scale could not read the 6 volts and would probably be ruined because it was not designed to read more than 1 volt.

When measuring the voltage of direct current electricity, it is necessary to notice the polarity of the meter.

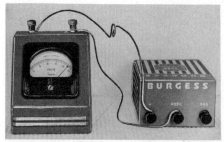

◆ 6. Measuring the voltage of a radio B battery. When connecting the meter it is necessary to observe the polarity of the battery and the meter. Minus goes to minus and plus goes to plus.

One terminal of the meter is marked with a + and is sometimes painted red. This is called the *positive* terminal of the meter and is connected to the positive terminal of the battery. The other terminal of the meter is connected to the *negative* post of the battery. The voltmeter is connected directly across the source of electricity. See Photograph 6.

Most homes use alternating current electricity and the voltage of the outlets is from 110 to 120 volts. When measuring the outlet voltage, an alternating current meter must be used. The scale can be a 0-to-150–volt or a 0-to-200–volt. See Photograph 7. Alternating current meters do not have a polarity marking as the direction of electron flow is always changing. The meter is connected directly across the outlet with one terminal of the meter going to one side of the outlet and the other terminal to the other side of the outlet.

Some meters called *multimeters* (Photograph 8) can be used for both alternating current and direct current. Separate connections are shown

◆ 7. Using an alternating current meter to measure the voltage of a wall outlet.

◆ 8. A multimeter that will measure ac and dc voltage, resistance, and direct current.

on the cases of the meters where the terminal leads may be connected for either ac or dc. These meters very often have various scales that can be selected by moving a switch on the front of the meter case.

INTERESTING THINGS TO DO

1. Measuring Direct Current Voltage.

Obtain a storage battery and a 0-to-15–volt direct current meter. Connect two insulated wires to the meter. Connect the positive terminal of the meter to the positive post of the storage battery. The other terminal is connected to the negative post of the battery. What is the voltage reading? What happens if you reverse the connections to the meter?

Measure the voltage of each cell of the battery by connecting the leads from the meter to the terminals of each cell. What is the voltage of the cells?

2. Measuring Home Outlet Voltage.

Obtain an ac meter with a 0-to-150–volt scale. Connect two insulated leads to each of the terminals of the meter. The other ends of these leads are connected to an attachment plug cap. Be sure the connectors are tight and that the wires do not touch each other. Plug the cap into the outlet voltage. What is the voltage reading?

3. Constructing a Neon Bulb Voltmeter.

Materials needed to construct the neon bulb voltmeter:

200,000-ohm, ½-watt carbon resistor
500,000-ohm carbon potentiometer
Pointer knob for potentiometer
Neon bulb, type NE–2
One pair of test leads about 3′ long
Hook-up wire

A 2″ length of mailing tube. This tube should be large enough in diameter for the potentiometer to fit in one end.

Cut a piece of cardboard the same diameter as the mailing tube. Make a hole in the center of this round disk large enough for the shaft of the potentiometer to fit through. Glue the round cardboard disk to the mailing tube. Cut a small oblong hole in the side of the mailing tube. Check to see that the hole will be large enough to see the neon bulb but not large enough to permit the bulb to come through the hole.

Before placing the parts in the mailing tube, solder all of the connections as shown in Drawing 10.

Place the parts inside the mailing tube and mount the potentiometer so that the shaft extends out of the end covered by the cardboard disk. This end of the tube can be covered with white paper as it will be where the dial markings are placed when calibrating the meter. The pointer knob

◆ 9. Neon Bulb Voltmeter

can be tightened on the potentiometer shaft.

Using a clear cement, glue the neon bulb inside the tube so that it is visible through the hole already cut in the tube.

Calibrating the Meter. Radio B batteries or a power supply with different voltages can be used to calibrate the meter. You should be careful when using this meter because the voltages used can cause a bad shock. When measuring voltage, it is important to avoid coming in contact with the terminals. Using a 90-volt B battery connect the two meter leads across the terminals of the battery. Turn the potentiometer to where the neon bulb just starts to glow. If the bulb is already glowing when the leads are connected, turn the potentiometer until the glow is almost out. At this point (where the glow starts to go out) place a mark on the end of the tubing. Label this mark "90 volts." The two test leads can be placed in a wall outlet and this voltage marked on the dial. The wall outlet voltage is usually about 117 volts. As in the B battery

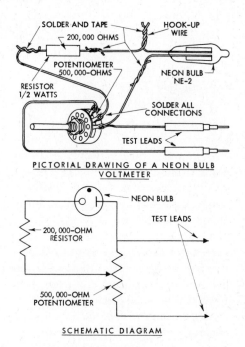

PICTORIAL DRAWING OF A NEON BULB VOLTMETER

SCHEMATIC DIAGRAM

◆ **10. Pictorial and Schematic Diagrams of a Neon Voltmeter**

voltage, the dial should be turned to the point when the glow starts to go out. Other known voltages can be marked on the dial. The meter will read up to 650 volts and as low as 70 volts.

REVIEW QUESTIONS

1. What is voltage?

2. Give another name for voltage.

3. List several devices that can produce a voltage.

4. What are the common voltages found in the home?

5. Draw a circuit showing where a voltmeter is placed in a circuit to measure the voltage or electromotive force.

6. When using alternating current voltmeters, why is it not necessary to have polarity markings on the meters?

7. What is the meter called that can measure both alternating and direct current as well as various voltages?

UNIT 10
MEASURING CURRENT

Current and Electron Flow

The flow of electricity is the movement of electrons in a circuit. This electron flow in a circuit is called *current* and if the electrons are always going in the same direction it is called *direct current*. *Alternating current* is a flow of electrons that is continuously changing directions.

To have a flow of electrons it is necessary to have a source of electricity, such as a generator, to provide the pressure or voltage to push the electrons through the circuit. These electrons go from the negative pole of the generator through the circuit and return to the positive pole of the generator.

Moving electrons might be compared to a bucket brigade used in putting out a fire. The source of water

is a well and after the bucket is filled, the people in the brigade pass it from one person to the next. The last person in line receives the bucket and pours the water on the fire. He then passes the bucket to another line of people who return it to the well to be filled again. Buckets are continuously being passed from one person to the next from the well to the fire and from the fire back to the well. This continuous movement of the buckets is like the flow of electrons which leave the source of electricity and flow through the circuit.

Electron Flow Measured in Amperes

In a city water system it is very common to measure the amount of water that is flowing through a pipe by determining the number of gal-

◆ 11. The small steel balls in the photograph represent electrons. The glass jar represents a battery with the negative side of the battery holding a large quantity of electrons (steel balls). The electrons leave the negative terminal of the battery, flow through the plastic tube and light bulb and return through the tube to the positive side of the battery. This flow of electrons from the negative terminal through the light bulb and back to the positive terminal produces light in the bulb. The flow of electrons is called *current*.

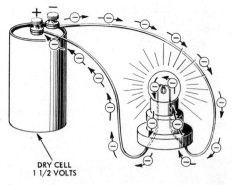

DRY CELL
1 1/2 VOLTS

◆ 12. This drawing indicates with arrows the flow of electrons from the negative terminal of the dry cell through the wire and light bulb back to the positive terminal. The circuit drawn here shows the same type of circuit that is illustrated with the steel balls in Photograph 11.

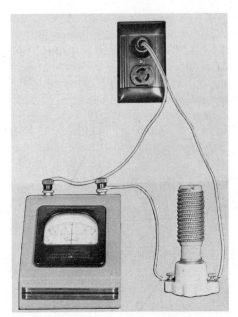

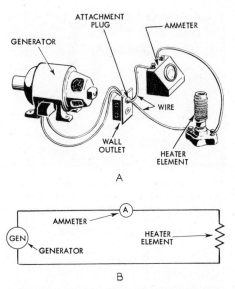

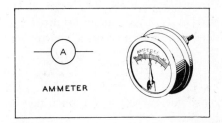

◆ 13. A heater element is plugged into a 115-volt alternating current wall outlet. Notice that one side of the wire going to the heater has been cut so that the ammeter can be connected in the circuit. The ammeter shows that a little more than 5 amperes of current is flowing through the element.

◆ 14. Drawing *A* shows the complete electrical circuit of Photograph 13. The generator is providing the voltage that is delivered by the two wires to the wall outlet. When the heater is connected to the outlet by an attachment plug, current flows in the circuit. The ammeter is connected in one side of the line to measure the current flow. Drawing *B* is a schematic diagram of the entire circuit. Symbols are used to represent the generator, ammeter, and heater element.

Ions that is flowing through the pipe in an hour. In electricity the electron flow is measured in amperes, which indicate the number of electrons that pass through the circuit in one second. Electrons are so very small that it takes about six million, million, million of them to pass through a circuit in one second to equal one ampere. Since this is such a large figure the quantity of current flow is stated in amperes. *Ampere* is the unit of measurement for current, the abbreviations being *amp* or *amps*.

Using Ammeters

An ammeter is used to measure the

electron flow in amperes. All ammeters are labeled as to whether they will read ac or dc. Just as in using a voltmeter it is important that the ammeter have the correct scale for the current to be measured.

To measure the current flow in a

The letter "A" in a symbol means ammeter.

◆ **15. The milliammeter indicates that 185 milliamperes is the amount of current flowing through the 1½-volt light bulb when it is connected to a flashlight cell. The 185 milliamperes is equal to .185 ampere.**

circuit the ammeter is connected in one wire of the line so that the electrons must flow through the meter as well as all of the rest of the circuit. Extreme care must be used to be sure that the voltage is not on when the meter is being connected.

Most direct current meters have a + marked on the positive connection. The other terminal is negative and should be connected to the negative side of the circuit. Alternating current ammeters do not have a polarity marking as they are made so that the electrons can flow through the meter in either direction.

When measuring current it is usually advisable to start with a meter that has a high ampere range. If the current is not enough to move the needle so that an accurate reading can be made, a smaller range meter can be used. Starting with a large range meter and then replacing with small range meter will avoid burning out the meter.

A common use of an ammeter is on the dashboard of some automobiles. The ammeter is used to show the driver whether the generator is charging or not. The meter is a center scale meter and indicates that no current is flowing through it when the needle is in the center of the dial. As the generator charges the battery of the automobile the needle moves to the right, showing that current is being supplied by the generator. When the generator is not charging the needle moves to the left. This shows the driver that the battery is providing the electricity and usually indicates that the automobile generator is not working.

In some circuits, such as a radio circuit, very small amounts of current flow and meters must be used that will read thousandths of an ampere. Meters which read current in thousandths of an ampere are called *milliammeters* (Photograph 15). *Milli* means one-thousandth. If a milliammeter has a scale of 0 to 300 this means that the meter will read from zero to three-hundred thousandths of an ampere. Three-hundred thousandths of an ampere is equal to three-tenths of an ampere.

TYPICAL CURRENT CONSUMPTION
Approximate currents used by some common home appliances are listed below:

Sewing machine	.80 ampere
Lamp bulbs (100-watt)	.83 ampere
Radio (small)	.85 ampere
Refrigerator	2.00 amperes
Television	2.00 amperes
Washing machine	2.50 amperes
Iron	6.60 amperes
¾ hp home air conditioning unit	12.00 amperes

Electroplating

Electrons will flow through certain chemical solutions the same as through wire conductors. This principle of current flow in solutions is used in *electroplating*. Electroplating is a very valuable commercial process used when metals need to be coated to prevent rust or to improve their appearance. Copper, nickel, silver, chromium, zinc, cadmium, and gold are the materials most often used in electroplating. The shiny chromium finish found on many automobile accessories is electroplated onto steel.

Electroplating solutions are usually made of a metallic salt solution such as copper sulfate for copper-plating, or nickel sulfate for nickel-plating. A direct current is always used in the plating process.

The object to be plated is placed in the electrolyte solution and is connected to the negative terminal of the direct current electricity. The positive terminal of the electricity is usually connected to a metal such as copper, nickel, or silver that is being used for the plating process. The object to be

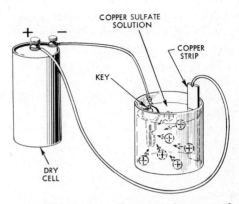

◆ 16. With the key and copper strip connected as shown, the positive copper particles dissolve and are then attracted by the negatively charged key. As the key is plated, the copper strip is worn away.

plated and the metal used for the plating are placed in the solution as shown in Illustration 16.

When direct current electricity is connected to the two metals, a current starts to flow through the metallic salt solution. The plating metal is dissolved into the solution. This makes the solution have an excess of metal particles which are pulled toward the material to be plated. As the metal particles reach the object a thin plating of the metal is placed on the object.

INTERESTING THINGS TO DO

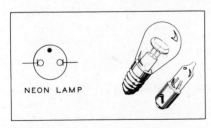

This symbol is used for an alternating current neon lamp.

1. Using a Neon Bulb as an Alternating or Direct Current Indicator.

Obtain a 105-125–volt neon lamp and socket for the lamp. Connect two wires from terminals on the socket to a 115-volt alternating current outlet. The lamp will light up immediately and both elements will appear to be lighted. Notice that there is a slight flickering glow from the elements. This flickering is due to the fluctuations of the alternating current.

Now connect the two socket leads of the neon lamp to a direct current source of electricity. This can be obtained from a 90-volt B battery. Notice that only one element of the lamp glows. Reverse the connections to the socket. What happens? How can we determine whether the current is alternating or direct with this neon bulb?

2. Constructing an Experimental Ammeter.

Material needed to construct the ammeter:

50' No. 26 magnet wire
Two washers (fiber or masonite), ¾" diameter
Tubing (cardboard, fiber, hard rubber), with hollow center, about ³⁄₁₆" to ¼" diameter x 1½" long
Pointer of tin, 2¾" x 3¼"
Back of plywood (or masonite), ¼" x 4½" x 7"
Base of pine, ¾" x 3" x 4½"
Plunger—round soft iron, ³⁄₁₆" x 2¼" (a 20-penny or 40-penny common nail can be used). Plunger must slide freely through the tubing.

Terminals—roundhead (RH) ½", No. 6 wood screws and soldering lugs or washers.

Construction. Drill holes in the two washers so that they will fit snugly over the tubing. Glue the washers to each end of the tubing. Wind the 50' of No. 26 magnet wire on the tubing. Even layers of wire will make a much nicer looking coil.

Make the meter holder by nailing the pine base to the plywood back. Refer to Drawing 18 for placement of the parts.

Cut the tin pointer as shown in the drawing. Punch a hole in the center with a shingle nail. To keep it from tilting, it is necessary to solder a small piece of tin to the back of the pointer. This tin strip is about ¼" wide and 1" long. It is soldered just below the center hole of the pointer and is bent as shown in the drawing. A small hole the same size as the pointer is punched in it so that the center nail must go through the pointer and the small tin strip. A shingle nail acts as the pivot and holds the pointer on to the back.

The coil is held to the back by two

◆ **17. Experimental Ammeter for Measuring the Current of a Light Bulb**

small pieces of wire at the top and bottom of the coil. Four small holes are drilled through the plywood back so that the wires can be tightened in the rear of the plywood. Solder the two leads from the coil to two terminals on the baseboard.

Check to be sure that the plunger ($\frac{3}{16}$″ x $2\frac{1}{4}$″ long) will slide freely through the center of the coil. Make a small hookeye on the top of the plunger by soldering a piece of copper wire to it. A thread is tied to the pointer and to the plunger so that when the pointer is centered the plunger will be about $\frac{1}{4}$″ inside the coil. Another piece of thread is tied to the other side of the pointer and the plunger is balanced by placing small pieces of solder through the thread loop.

Calibrating the Meter. The experimental meter may be calibrated by using a group of light bulbs of a known wattage.

Wire three light bulb sockets in parallel. The terminals on the meter should be connected in one side of a pair of leads that can be plugged into a 115-volt outlet.

Obtain three electric light bulbs—two 25-watt bulbs and one 50-watt bulb.

Screw in the 50-watt bulb. The bulb will burn and the pointer of the meter will move toward the left. Place a mark at that point. This mark shows about .41 ampere of current. With the 50-watt bulb still burning, screw in a 25-watt bulb in the second socket. The pointer will move farther to the left. The meter is now reading about .62 ampere and the dial should again

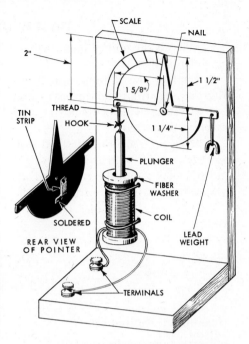

◆ 18. Drawing of the Experimental Ammeter

be labeled. Now screw in the other 25-watt bulb. The pointer will again move and the current flow will be about .82 ampere. The ammeter is now calibrated and can be used to make other measurements.

3. Copper-Plating an Object.

Fill a glass jar (pint size) with a solution of copper sulfate. Place a strip of sheet copper about 1″ wide and 4″ long in one side of the jar. In the other side of the jar place the object to be plated such as a key, or piece of iron. Using a dry cell connect the positive terminal to the copper strip and the negative terminal to the object to be plated. Current will flow in the circuit and the plating process will start. After about 15 minutes remove the object from the solution. What has happened?

REVIEW QUESTIONS

1. What is the unit of measurement of electron flow?

2. Explain the difference between alternating current and direct current.

3. Give the name of the meter used to measure current.

4. Draw a circuit of a dry cell connected to a light bulb and show where the ammeter should be connected.

5. Why is it important to have the voltage off when connecting meters?

6. What does the term *milli* mean?

7. If a circuit has a .150 ampere of current flowing in it, how many milli-amperes is that?

8. What type of current is used for electroplating?

9. Why is electroplating a very valuable process to many manufacturers of metal objects?

UNIT 11
MEASURING RESISTANCE

Meaning of Resistance

Every complete electrical circuit includes wire and a device that consumes current. The voltage forces the current through the circuit. The wire and the current-consuming device, such as a lamp, provide what is called *resistance*. Resistance is the opposition to electron flow that is found in every circuit.

Electrical resistance can be called friction. Electrical friction might be compared to friction which tends to keep things in motion from moving freely. Automobiles traveling on a

highway have friction between the pavement and the tires, boats have friction when moving in water, and friction is developed when an airplane flies through the air. In all of these examples, friction is slowing down the object.

In electricity, the friction or resistance developed by the flow of electrons in a circuit tends to reduce the amount of current flow. The greater the resistance in a circuit, the less the current flow, just as the increased friction developed when an automobile drives off a paved highway onto a dirt road tends to slow it down. The resistance in a circuit can be increased if the length of the wire used in the circuit is made longer, since this will lengthen the path over which the electrons must flow. If the wire is made smaller this too will increase the resistance since it will provide a smaller

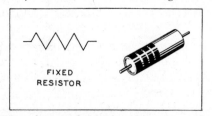

FIXED RESISTOR

The resistor symbol begins with an up-stroke.

path for the electrons to flow through.

How Resistance Produces Heat

Electrical resistance has many uses. One of the most important uses of resistance is its ability to make electricity produce heat. Heat is produced by friction. This can be demonstrated if we rub two wooden blocks together very rapidly. The blocks will become warm owing to the friction caused by the rubbing. In electricity, the electrons that are flowing through the wires hit each other, and this collision of electrons results in heat being developed the same as by the rubbing of the blocks together.

We can increase the heating effect of electricity if we can increase the amount of current flow. Current flow can be increased by adding additional voltage or pressure to the circuit. The greater the electron flow the greater the friction from the electrons coming in contact with each other and thus the greater the heat developed.

We are all familiar with the use of electricity in many types of heating appliances such as electric stoves, hot water heaters, flat irons, waffle irons, toasters, and electric blankets. In these appliances (Photograph 19) a special

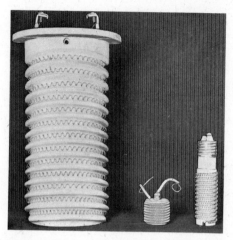

◆ 19. Examples of three types of heating elements. The large element on the left is used in a wall heater; the small element in the center is used to heat a coffee percolator; the element on the right is used in a portable room heater. All of these elements use coiled nichrome mounted on a ceramic base.

resistance wire called *nichrome* is used to produce heat. Nichrome is an alloy of nickel and chromium and has a high resistance to electron flow. This high resistance plus its ability to be very hot without melting makes it ideal for use as a heater element.

The light bulb, called an *incandescent lamp* (Illustration 20), also uses the heating effect of electricity to produce light. The lamp has a wire

RHEOSTAT

The arrow across the symbol indicates that the resistor is variable.

OHM

OHMMETER

This is how to indicate the instrument for measuring resistance in ohms.

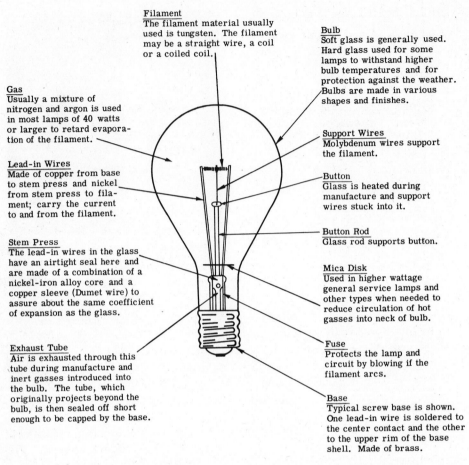

Filament
The filament material usually used is tungsten. The filament may be a straight wire, a coil or a coiled coil.

Bulb
Soft glass is generally used. Hard glass used for some lamps to withstand higher bulb temperatures and for protection against the weather. Bulbs are made in various shapes and finishes.

Gas
Usually a mixture of nitrogen and argon is used in most lamps of 40 watts or larger to retard evaporation of the filament.

Support Wires
Molybdenum wires support the filament.

Lead-in Wires
Made of copper from base to stem press and nickel from stem press to filament; carry the current to and from the filament.

Button
Glass is heated during manufacture and support wires stuck into it.

Stem Press
The lead-in wires in the glass have an airtight seal here and are made of a combination of a nickel-iron alloy core and a copper sleeve (Dumet wire) to assure about the same coefficient of expansion as the glass.

Button Rod
Glass rod supports button.

Mica Disk
Used in higher wattage general service lamps and other types when needed to reduce circulation of hot gasses into neck of bulb.

Exhaust Tube
Air is exhausted through this tube during manufacture and inert gasses introduced into the bulb. The tube, which originally projects beyond the bulb, is then sealed off short enough to be capped by the base.

Fuse
Protects the lamp and circuit by blowing if the filament arcs.

Base
Typical screw base is shown. One lead-in wire is soldered to the center contact and the other to the upper rim of the base shell. Made of brass.

Courtesy Sylvania Electric Products, Inc.

◆ **20. In the incandescent lamp, light results from the heating effect of electrical resistance.**

inside of the glass bulb called a *filament*. This filament is made of a high resistance wire made of tungsten. As the electrons flow through the tungsten the friction of the electrons produces heat. This heat is so great that the filament becomes white hot and gives off light. To keep the tungsten filament from burning up because of the oxygen in the air, it is placed in a glass bulb. All of the air is then removed from the bulb and the filament can get very hot without burning up.

Resistance Used to Control Current Flow and Reduce Voltage

Very often it is desirable to be able to control the amount of electricity used by a device. A good example of this is stage lighting where it is necessary to dim the lights. If the amount of current flowing through the lights can be reduced then the lights will become dimmer. We can reduce the current flow by putting more resistance in the circuit. The resistance can be a specially constructed resistor of nichrome wire. The resistor is connected in the circuit as shown in Illustration 21, so that the current must flow through the resistor and the light bulb. In this way the quantity of electrons flowing through the lamp is reduced by the resistor. The light is dimmed because part of the voltage delivered by the wall outlet is being reduced by the resistor. If we want to vary the brightness of the light a variable resistor called a *rheostat* must be used.

A rheostat has a movable contact arm that makes it possible to change the amount of resistance in the circuit (Photographs 22 and 23). When the contact arm is moved to the extreme left the entire voltage is available for the lamp and it burns brightly. As the contact arm moves to the right (clockwise) more resistance is placed in the circuit and the lamp becomes dimmer. The increased resistance lowers the current flow and the resistor reduces the voltage.

Rheostats are used to control the speed of motors. The speed of electric sewing machines is controlled through the use of a variable resistor that can be moved with the knee or foot. As the rheostat is pushed down it decreases the amount of resistance and allows more voltage to be used to speed up the sewing machine motor.

Resistance Measurement

The unit of measurement of resistance is the *ohm*. Some circuits have a very few ohms resistance whereas others may have a million ohms resistance. All circuits have resistance in the wire and in the device using the electricity.

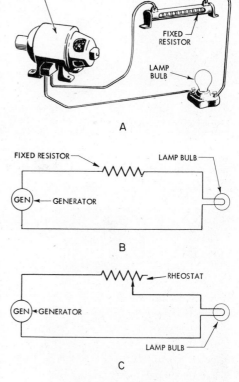

◆ 21. (A) The fixed resistor in the circuit reduces the current flow through the lamp bulb. The light from the lamp is dimmer because part of the voltage is used by the fixed resistor. (B) A wiring diagram using electrical symbols to represent the circuit shown in *A*. (C) This schematic diagram shows how a rheostat is used in a circuit to vary the brightness of a lamp bulb.

♦ 22. The lamp is burning brightly as the contact arm of the rheostat is allowing all of the current to flow directly to the lamp. The voltmeter connected across the lamp reads about 117 volts.

Where fairly heavy current is flowing fixed resistors are made of nichrome wire. If small amounts of current are flowing through the circuit, such as in many radio circuits, fixed resistors made of carbon can be used.

♦ 23. The contact or arm has been moved so that the current must flow through part of the rheostat before going to the lamp. The rheostat has provided enough resistance to reduce the voltage across the lamp to about 60 volts. The light from the lamp is dimmer.

Variable resistors are also made of nichrome wire or carbon, depending upon the amount of current to be controlled.

Resistance can be measured directly by the use of a meter called an *ohmmeter*. Some multimeters used to measure voltage and current are also used as ohmmeters. A very accurate device used to measure resistance is called a *Wheatstone bridge*.

Care must be used in measuring resistance with an ohmmeter to be sure that the voltage has been disconnected from the circuit. Leaving the voltage on when measuring the resistance will damage the ohmmeter.

In circuits where heat is developed the true resistance cannot be measured with an ohmmeter. As wires heat they increase their opposition to electron flow and the resistance in the circuit is increased. To determine the resistance of circuits where heat is being developed Ohm's law, which will be explained in Unit 13, must be used.

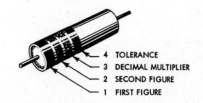

    4 TOLERANCE
    3 DECIMAL MULTIPLIER
    2 SECOND FIGURE
    1 FIRST FIGURE

◆ **24. Composition Resistor Color-Coding**

Color-Coding

Resistors for use in circuits usually have the resistance marked on them. The markings may be in numerals or in the form of color codes as shown in Illustration 24. A composition fixed resistor usually has a tan body with three or four colored stripes on one end. The first two indicate the first two figures of the ohmic value. The third stripe designates the number by which those figures must be multiplied. The tolerance (how much the resistor may vary from its rated value) is indicated by the last stripe. If there is no fourth stripe, the tolerance is plus or minus 20%. The values indicated by the colors are taken from a table.

INTERESTING THINGS TO DO

Constructing an Experimental Ohmmeter.

Materials needed to construct the ohmmeter:

85' No. 32 magnet wire
Cardboard tubing, 1½" inside diameter x 2" long
Wood base, ½" x 3" x 5"
Pointer of sheet brass, 2⅝" x ⅛"
Piece of hacksaw blade, 3/16" x 1⅜"
Sheet brass, ½" x 1¾" (2 required)
Sheet brass, ⅝" x 1½" (2 required)

Construction. Shape the two brass pointer bearings as shown in Drawing

26. Center-punch the upper ends of the bearings and secure them to the wood base with wood screws ½" apart. Cut the meter pointer to the shape shown in the drawing. Cut a small steel brad and sharpen the ends so that it will turn freely between the pointer bearings. Drill a hole the size of the steel brad through the brass pointer ¾" from the square end. Drill a similar hole through the center of the piece of hacksaw blade. Harden the piece of hacksaw blade by heating

◆ 25. An Experimental Ohmmeter

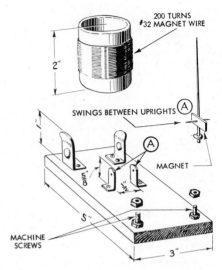

◆ 26. Drawing of the Experimental Ohmmeter

it to a cherry red over a flame, then plunging it into cold water. Solder the meter pointer and piece of hacksaw blade to the steel brad so that the two pieces will be at a right angle to each other. Secure a loop of solder to the lower end of the meter pointer, place the pointer between the bearings and test it for balance. The pointer should swing freely between the bearings and come to rest in an exact upright position. If it is necessary to lighten either end of the piece of hacksaw blade it may be done with a grinder or file, but care must be used because the hardened steel may break easily. After the pointer has been checked for balance, the piece of hacksaw blade may be magnetized by stroking it with a magnet as described in another part of this book.

Wind about 200 turns of magnet wire around the center of the cardboard tubing. Drill two small holes through the wood base through which to pass the coil ends and glue the coil to the wood base. Make certain that

the coil does not touch the ends of the piece of hacksaw blade.

Shape two pieces of sheet brass to hold a flashlight cell and secure them to the wood base as shown in the drawing. Secure two machine screws at the end of the wood base to serve as terminal screws. Connect a piece of magnet wire on the bottom of the wood base between one of the flashlight cell holders and one end of the coil. Connect the other flashlight support to a screw terminal. Connect the other end of the coil to the other screw terminal. Secure a piece of white cardboard to the top of the coil to serve as a meter scale. Secure two pieces of flexible wire to the meter terminals to serve as test leads. The meter is now ready to be calibrated.

Calibrating the Ohmmeter. Place a flashlight cell in the holder and touch the two ends of the flexible leads together. The meter pointer will now swing to an extreme right or left position, depending upon which way the flashlight cell was placed in its holder. This is called the "zero" position and should be marked on the cardboard scale with the figure "0". Secure a 60-watt mazda lamp and touch the ends of the meter test leads to the contacts at the base of the lamp. The meter pointer will swing away from its center position and come to rest at a point toward the "0" position. Since the cold resistance of the 60-watt lamp is 20 ohms, write the figure "20" on the meter scale directly above the meter pointer. Other figures for calibrating the meter may be obtained from other size lamps and household electrical appliances. A 25-watt lamp has a cold resistance of about 50 ohms, while a 100-watt lamp has a cold resistance of only 10 ohms. A spiral heating element such as is used in an electric heater has a cold resistance of about 20 ohms.

REVIEW QUESTIONS

1. What is resistance?

2. What happens to the resistance of a circuit if a large diameter wire is replaced with a smaller diameter wire?

3. How does resistance produce heat?

4. Name the material used for heater elements.

5. Why is it necessary to keep the air away from the filament of an incandescent lamp?

6. What is a variable resistor called?

7. What is the unit of measurement of resistance called?

8. Explain what happens to the resistance of a heater element when the current is turned on.

UNIT 12
USING CONDUCTORS AND INSULATORS

Common Conductors

We have stated that wires are used to provide a path through which electrons flow. These wires are called *conductors* because they conduct the electricity to the various parts of the circuit. Conductors are usually made of metal since most metals permit electrons to flow through them easily. Some liquids are conductors of electricity but are used only for special purposes such as the electrolyte in storage batteries and electroplating.

All metals are conductors of electricity but some have more resistance than others. Copper is one of the metals which has a low resistance. Silver has a slightly lower resistance than copper but because it is more expensive than copper it is used only in special types of circuits. Almost all circuits use copper wire for conduc-

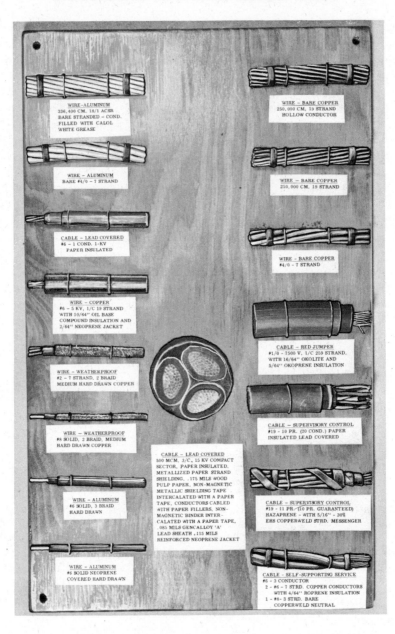

◆ 27. Conductors used for power distribution are made to meet the requirements of different conditions.

tors, as it is an excellent conductor that is fairly plentiful and not too expensive.

Aluminum has a higher resistance than copper but is occasionally used when extremely light weight is needed. Long power transmission lines are sometimes made of aluminum to reduce the weight of the wire.

Since all metals are conductors, different metals are sometimes used where they can supply special needs. These metals and some of their uses are listed below. They are listed according to their resistance with the first, silver, having the lowest resistance and the last, carbon, having the highest resistance.

CONDUCTORS	TYPICAL APPLICATIONS
Silver	Circuit breaker contacts, electronic circuits
Copper	All types of electrical conductors
Gold	Electroscope leaves
Aluminum	Lightweight conductors
Tungsten	Radio and lamp filaments
Zinc	Fuses and dry cells
Brass	Wall plugs and other types of exposed electrical connections
Nickel	Radio tubes
Tin	Solder
Steel	Telephone and telegraph lines
Lead	Solder and storage battery plates
Mercury	Switches
Nichrome	Heater elements
Carbon	Arc lamps and motor brushes

Measuring Wire Sizes

All conductors have resistance. Large conductors have less resistance than small conductors because the electrons have more freedom to move in the large conductors. Long conductors have more resistance than short conductors (of the same size) because the electrons have a longer path to flow through in the long conductor.

Since resistance can reduce the amount of electricity that flows in a circuit, it is often necessary to have conductors which will provide very little opposition to electron flow. To help in selecting the correct conductor all wires are designated according to number size. The smaller the number the larger the wire. A No. 8 wire is about $\frac{1}{8}''$ in diameter and is much larger than a No. 14 wire which is about $\frac{1}{16}''$ in diameter. A No. 36 wire is extremely small and is about the diameter of a human hair.

Wire sizes may be measured by a gage called a *wire gage* (Photograph 28). Gages used in the United States are called *American Standard Wire Gages.*

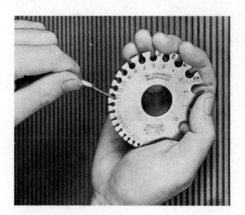

◆ 28. Using a wire gage to determine the size of a wire. The size of wire is found by placing the wire between the slots on the outside edge of the gage. The slot in which the wire fits snugly indicates the gage of the wire. The round hole at the bottom of the slot makes it easier to remove the wire after checking for size.

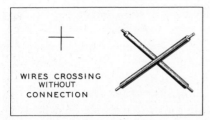

Wires crossing without connection are shown this way.

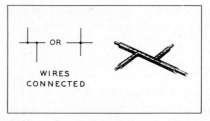

A dot is used to indicate a junction between wires.

Use of the correct wire size for different circuits is necessary to prevent loss due to resistance and to keep the wire from heating. If the wire used is too small for the amount of current flowing in the circuit, heat will be produced. This heat from excess current in wires can produce a fire and has been the cause of many houses burning down. Each electrical device and every circuit in the home uses a size wire that will carry the current safely. It is important to know how much current each circuit will be using in order to select the proper size wire.

Wire may be obtained either solid or stranded. Solid wire is usually used for wiring homes and in places where the wires do not need to be moved. Stranded wire is made up of several small wires twisted together. By using several small wires together it is possible to have a very flexible wire that can be moved easily. All large cables used for transmission lines are stranded. Cords used on home appliances and extension cords are stranded so that the cords can be moved and coiled readily.

The following table shows several wire sizes and gives some common uses for these sizes.

SIZE OF WIRE	COMMON USE
6 to 10	Service leads for light and power to homes
12 to 14	Interior house wiring
16 to 18	Lighting fixtures
18 to 20	Bell wire, radio circuits
20 to 24	Motors, door chimes
24 to 30	Radio coils, small motors

The diameter and resistance for the even sizes of copper from No. 6 to No. 30 are listed in the following table.

COPPER WIRE SIZE	DIAMETER OF WIRE	RESISTANCE IN OHMS FOR 100 FEET OF WIRE
6	.162	.0403
8	.128	.0641
10	.102	.102
12	.081	.162
14	.064	.258
16	.051	.409
18	.040	.651
20	.032	1.00
22	.025	1.65
24	.024	2.62
26	.016	4.16
28	.013	6.62
30	.010	10.5

Purpose of Insulators

Materials which do not permit electrons to flow through them are called *nonconductors* or *insulators*. These insulators are nonmetallic. In electrical circuits insulators are just as important as conductors. Conductors provide a definite path through which electrons will flow; insulators are used

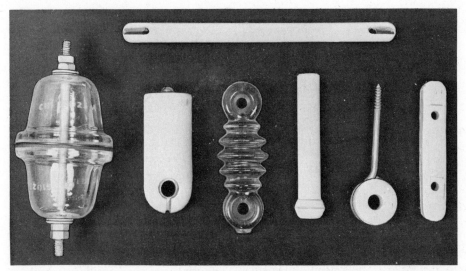

◆ 29. Insulators are designed for special purposes; without them, electricity could not be used.

to prevent the electrons from flowing where they are not wanted.

Insulation is necessary in most electrical wiring to avoid short circuits. Short circuits occur when wires or bare electrical contacts touch each other so that an unwanted path is made through which current can flow. These unwanted paths allow the current to flow through them instead of through the regular circuit. The wires used in electrical circuits in the home are covered with insulation so that they can be placed next to each other without causing a "short circuit." Should the bare copper wires touch each other the electrons would stop flowing through the necessary parts of the circuit. Most wires are covered with enamel, cotton, rubber, or plastic materials. The type of material selected for wire insulation depends upon where the wire is going to be used. Heavy insulation is needed on wires

◆ 30. This is how insulators are installed on power poles.

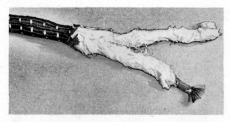

◆ 31. A photograph showing asbestos insulation in a heater cord. Each wire is wrapped in asbestos, which will not burn.

that will rub or come in contact with other objects or where high voltages are used.

Insulation is needed to protect people from coming into contact with electrical circuits. All switches must be insulated so that people may turn them off and on without receiving a shock from the electricity. Wall outlets are insulated so that they will not shock anyone that touches them.

Types of Insulators

There are many types of insulators. Each is used for a specific purpose. Air is a good insulator and is used where space is not a problem and where people cannot touch the circuit. Air is actually the insulation between the wires that are strung on high power transmission lines.

Circuits carrying very high voltages require extremely good insulators. The pressure from high voltages can make the electrons jump from one part of the circuit to another the same as lightning jumps between the sky and the ground. High-voltage transmission lines use large glass or ceramic insulators on the power poles (Photograph 30). These insulators prevent the electricity from flowing

through the poles to the ground. Power poles made of wood become very good conductors of electricity when wet.

In circuits where heat is involved asbestos, ceramic, and mica are used for insulation. Wire cords connected to heater elements, such as in flat irons, are usually covered with asbestos and cotton. The asbestos will not burn and is a very good insulator for electricity. See Photograph 31. Mica and ceramic materials are used as a base to hold the heater elements made of nichrome wire in toasters, flat irons, and all types of electrical heaters. Both materials are good insulators and can withstand tremendous heat without burning or melting.

Special types of insulators are needed in high-frequency radio circuits. These high-frequency waves have the ability to make electrons flow through some types of insulation. Materials such as steatite and polystyrene are often used in high-frequency circuits since they are good insulators for this purpose.

The following are some common insulators and their uses:

INSULATOR	COMMON USE
Air	Between transmission lines
Paper	To separate windings in transformers and motors
Enamel	Covering on magnet wire
Fiber	Motors, solenoids
Mica	Toasters, separation for radio capacitors
Rubber	Wire covering
Bakelite	Electrical outlets and switches
Ceramics	Heater element bases, transmission lines
Plastic	Wire covering
Steatite	Television, radio
Oil	Transformers and capacitors

INTERESTING THINGS TO DO

1. Making a Pigtail Splice.

Skin the wire ends about 2", as shown at *A,* Illustration 34. Cross the cleaned bare ends just below the end of the insulation, *B.* Hold the ends with the fingers and thumb of one hand, and twisting them together with the other hand, make about six turns, *C.* Trim the ends, as shown at *D.* Solder the splice, *E* and *F.* After the wire has cooled, wipe it with a damp cloth and insulate the splice with Scotch Electrical Tape.

◆ 32. When removing insulation with a knife, use a fairly sharp knife and cut the insulation at an angle of about 30 degrees. Do not circle the wire with the blade at right angles to it. Usually, this produces a groove or nick in the wire which will cause it to break easily when bent at this point. Also a nick in the wire may reduce its capacity to carry current. Use a wire stripper to remove insulation whenever possible.

◆ 33. Pigtail splices are used where wires are to be joined together. The splice is usually placed in a junction box. The joint is always soldered and taped before the cover is placed on the box.

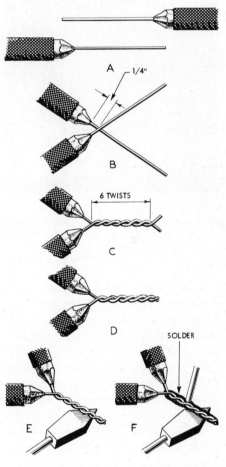

◆ 34. This is how to make a pigtail splice.

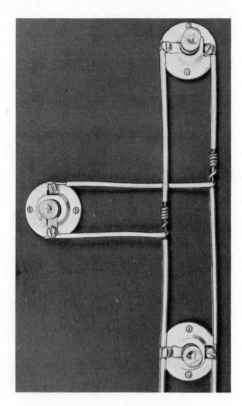

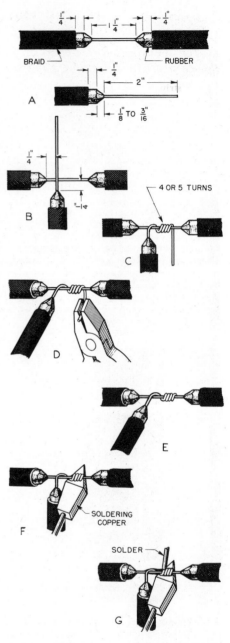

◆ 35. A tee-tap splice is used where it is necessary to connect onto an existing circuit. The tee-tap makes it possible to splice onto the wire without cutting it.

2. Making a Tee-Tap Splice.

Remove the insulation from the wires, *A*, Illustration 36. Cross the wires, as shown at *B*. Wrap the branch wire around the main wire, *C*. Wind the wire tightly with pliers, *D*. Cut off the projecting end of the wire, leaving no sharp projection, *E*. Solder the splice, as shown at *F* and *G*. After the wire has cooled, wipe it with a damp cloth and insulate the splice with Scotch Electrical Tape.

◆ 36. This is how to make a tee-tap splice.

◆ 37. A Western Union splice is used where wire needs to be lengthened.

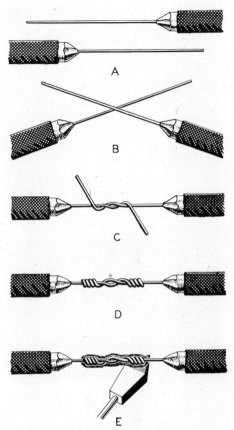

◆ 38. These are the steps to follow in making a Western Union splice.

3. Making a Western Union Splice.

Remove the insulation from the ends of the wires for a distance of about 3″, *A,* Illustration 38. Cross the two wires, as shown at *B.* Twist the wires around each other, so as to make two complete turns, *C.* Wrap the projecting ends around the straight sections of the wires so as to make three close turns, *D.* Wind the wire tightly with pliers and cut off the remaining ends. Solder the splice, as shown at *E.* After the wire has cooled, wipe it with a damp cloth and insulate the splice with Scotch Electrical Tape.

REVIEW QUESTIONS

1. Why is copper used most often as a conductor?

2. Where is aluminum used as a conductor?

3. What metal has the lowest resistance?

4. In wire sizes, which is larger in diameter, a No. 10 wire or a No. 12?

5. Why is it important to use the correct size wire when wiring a home?

6. What is the resistance of 50′ of No. 30 wire?

7. Give the purpose of insulators in a circuit.

8. List several commercial-type insulating materials.

9. What is the difference between conductors and insulators?

UNIT 13

SHOWING THE RELATIONSHIP OF VOLTAGE, CURRENT, AND RESISTANCE

Importance of Ohm's Law

In every electrical circuit we have three basic measurements:

1. *Voltage* —The pressure that forces electrons through the circuit.

2. *Current* —The amount of electrons flowing.

3. *Resistance*—The opposition to electron flow.

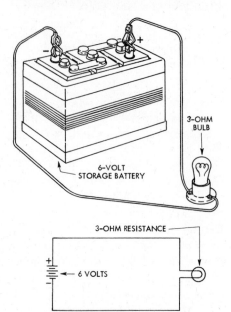

Before connecting a circuit it is often important to know what each of these measurements will be. By knowing what the current flow is we can select the proper size wire. By knowing what the voltage is we can select the correct size device that will work from the known voltage. It would be very time-consuming if every electrical circuit had to be tried out experimentally before it was possible to determine the amount of voltage, current, or resistance in the circuit. If we are to work efficiently with electricity we must be able to calculate the electrical measurements of the circuit before we hook them up.

There is a definite relationship between the voltage, current, and resistance in every circuit. When the voltage is increased the current will also be increased since more voltage will provide more pressure to push electrons through the circuit. If more resistance is added to a circuit this will reduce the amount of current, as

◆ 39. Six-volt storage battery connected to a light bulb with 3 ohms resistance.

there will be more opposition to electron flow. Whenever any change is made in either the voltage or resistance this changes the current flow.

This relationship that exists between the three electrical measurements can be calculated mathematically by a law called *Ohm's law*. Ohm's law is a mathematical formula that is used to calculate the current flow if the voltage and resistance of the circuit are known; it is used to determine the voltage if the current and resistance are known; and it is used to calculate the resistance if the voltage and current are known. From this we can see that if any two measurements are known the third measurement can be determined.

Calculating Current Flow

Ohm's law states that the *current is equal to the voltage divided by the resistance*. This can be shown mathematically as

Current (in amperes) =

$$\frac{\text{Voltage (in volts)}}{\text{Resistance (in ohms)}}$$

In the circuit in Illustration 39 the voltage of the storage battery is 6 volts. The resistance of the bulb is 3 ohms. How much current will flow in the circuit? Using the formula

$$\text{Current} = \frac{\text{Voltage}}{\text{Resistance}}$$

Voltage is 6 volts

Resistance is 3 ohms

Placing the numbers in the formula:

$$\text{Current} = \frac{6}{3}$$

$$\text{Current} = 2 \text{ amperes}$$

In Ohm's law as in most mathematical formulas symbols are used for each of the measurements.

The letter I is used for current in amperes.

The letter E is used for voltage in volts.

The letter R is used for resistance in ohms.

Ohm's law formula:

$$\text{Current} = \frac{\text{Voltage}}{\text{Resistance}}$$

Ohm's law formula with symbols:

$$I = \frac{E}{R}$$

Devices connected to a source of voltage are often shown in a diagram as being a resistor. The pictorial drawing in Illustration 40 shows a generator connected to a searchlight. The line drawing using symbols is called a *schematic diagram* and shows the searchlight as a resistor.

If the generator is producing 50 volts and the resistance of the searchlight is 5 ohms how much current would be flowing in the circuit?

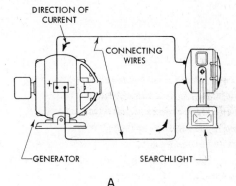

A

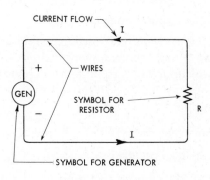

B

◆ 40. The generator supplies current to the searchlight, which acts as a resistor.

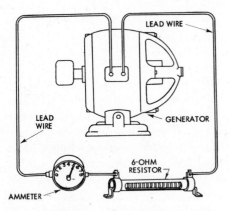

◆ 41. A current of 5 amperes is flowing through a resistance of 6 ohms.

Ohm's law formula $I = \dfrac{E}{R}$

Placing numbers in the formula

$$I = \dfrac{50}{5}$$

$$I = 10 \text{ amperes}$$

The current flowing in the circuit would be 10 amperes.

Calculating Voltage

Ohm's law can be used to determine the voltage being applied to a circuit provided the current and resistance are known. The formula for determining the voltage is:

Voltage = Current × Resistance

Using symbols $E = I \times R$

In the circuit in Illustration 41 the current is 5 amperes. The resistance is 6 ohms. What is the voltage of the generator?

$$E = I \times R$$
$$E = 5 \times 6$$
$$E = 30 \text{ volts}$$

The voltage of the generator is 30 volts.

Calculating Resistance

Ohm's law can be used to calculate the resistance in a circuit if the voltage and the current are known. The formula for calculating resistance is:

Resistance is equal to voltage divided by the current.

$$\text{Resistance (ohms)} = \frac{\text{Voltage (volts)}}{\text{Current (amperes)}}$$

Using symbols $R = \dfrac{E}{I}$

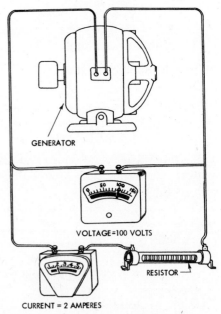

◆ 42. The generator is producing 100 volts and 2 amperes of current is flowing through the resistor.

In the circuit in Illustration 42 the voltage is 100 volts. The current is 2 amperes. The circuit resistance is

$$R = \frac{E}{I} = \frac{100}{2} = 50 \text{ ohms}$$

The resistances of wire and other types of electrical conductors increase when they become heated. A lamp filament has a much greater resistance when it is giving off light than when it is cold. The resistance of a heated conductor is known as its "hot" resistance.

Refer to pages 242-243 for formulas used in calculating the resistance in different kinds of circuits.

The Three Forms of Ohm's Law

Ohm's law can be used for three different purposes:

To find the current $I = \dfrac{E}{R}$

To find the voltage $E = I \times R$

To find the resistance $R = \dfrac{E}{I}$

If any two of the electrical measurements are known the third measurement can be determined.

Measuring Electrical Power

The *watt* is the electrical unit of power. Power means the ability to do work. We are all familiar with the unit of work called *horsepower* used with automobiles. In automobiles it is customary to state the amount of horsepower that the engine will produce. A 175-horsepower engine is more powerful and will do more work than a 100-horsepower engine. In electricity the wattage indicates the power being used by the electrical device.

Electric light bulbs are marked according to the number of watts of electricity they use. The greater the wattage of the bulb the greater the amount of light produced. A 25-watt electric light bulb will not burn as brightly nor will it use as much electricity as a 100-watt bulb. A 75-watt electric soldering iron will not get as hot as a 100-watt soldering iron. A 600-watt electric wall heater will not heat a room as fast as a 1,000-watt heater. In each of these items the lower wattage produces less power in the form of heat or light, and uses less electricity. From this we can see that it is important to look at the wattage rating on all electrical equipment that we plan to buy or use.

Calculating Wattage

The power or wattage used by electrical circuits can be calculated mathematically. The basic formula for determining wattage states that *the number of watts used equals the voltage across the circuit multiplied by the current flowing in the circuit.*

Basic watt formula

Watts = Voltage × Current

Using symbols

$$W = E \times I$$

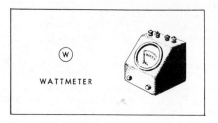

WATTMETER

This symbol indicates an instrument for measuring power.

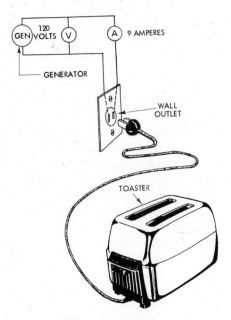

GENERATOR

WALL
OUTLET

TOASTER

◆ 43. The amount of electricity used is measured in watts.

In the circuit in Illustration 43 the toaster has 9 amperes of current flowing through it and the voltage at the electrical outlet is 120 volts. What is the wattage of the toaster?

Basic formula

Watts = Voltage × Current

$$W = E \times I$$

(Placing numbers in the formula)

Volts = 120

Amperes = 9

$$W = 120 \times 9$$

$$W = 1080 \text{ Watts}$$

The toaster is using 1,080 watts of electricity.

The instruments used to calculate the wattage are a voltmeter and an ammeter. A single meter called a wattmeter which is a combination volt-

◆ 44. The wattmeter on the left shows that the heater element is using a little more than 600 watts of electricity. If a wattmeter is not available a voltmeter and an ammeter may be used to determine the wattage of the circuit. The voltmeter reads about 120 volts. The ammeter reads about 5 amperes. Using the watt formula the power can be calculated by multiplying the voltage times the current. Thus, 120 volts times 5 amperes equals 600 watts.

meter and ammeter can be used to measure the wattage of a circuit. With this meter it is not necessary to use the watt formula. When connected in the circuit a wattmeter scale reading shows the amount of wattage being used by the circuit.

Meaning of Kilowatt

The term *kilowatt* is sometimes used to express power used by electrical equipment. *Kilo* means 1,000. One kilowatt equals 1,000 watts. Ten kilowatts equals 10,000 watts. If an electrical heater has a name plate that states that the heater uses 3 kilowatts of electricity this means that it uses 3,000 watts of electricity.

Using Watt-Hour Meters

The power company that delivers electricity to homes and businesses

Courtesy General Electric Co.

◆ 45. This watt-hour meter records the amount of electricity used.

throughout a community uses a meter called a *watt-hour* meter at each location. The meter is connected so that all the electricity goes through it

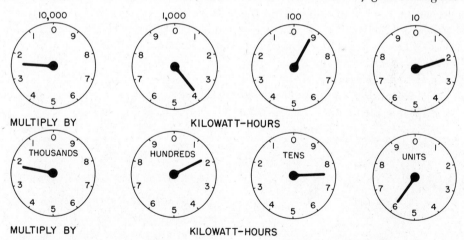

◆ 46. This is how to read a watt-hour meter. Record the figure which the pointer on the right-hand dial has last passed and proceed to the left, recording in like manner the respective figure indicated on each successive dial. Thus, the top meter would read, 2,392 (setting numbers down right to left —2, —92, -392, 2,392) and the bottom one 2,176. Let the bottom dial represent the meter reading at the beginning of the month and the top one that at the end of the month. Thus 2,392— 2,176 = 216 kilowatt-hours used for the month.

before going into the building. Each meter is so constructed that it measures the wattage and also operates like a stop watch that runs only when the current is being used. Thus the meter is keeping a record of the amount of time that it is being used. The dials on the face of the meter record the number of kilowatt-hours flowing into the building. The exact number of kilowatt-hours of electricity consumed can be determined at any time by reading the meter. Power companies have a rate that they charge for each kilowatt-hour of electricity. Electric bills are figured by determining the number of kilowatt-hours consumed and multiplying this by the rate charged.

INTERESTING THINGS TO DO

1. Determining the Hot Resistance of an Electric Light Bulb.

Materials needed are a 100-watt light bulb, lamp socket, attachment plug, insulated wire, ac voltmeter and an ac ammeter.

Connect the circuit as shown in Illustration 47. The voltmeter and ammeter constructed in Units 9 and 10 may be used. After measuring the voltage and the current use Ohm's law to calculate the resistance of the lamp bulb. How will this resistance differ from the cold resistance of the lamp?

2. Determining the Current Used by a Heater Element.

Materials needed are a lamp socket, a screw-base type 600-watt heater element, attachment plug, ac voltmeter, and ac ammeter.

Wire the circuit as shown in Illustration 48. The resistance of the heater element is approximately 20 ohms. After measuring the voltage calculate the current flow using Ohm's law. Prove your answer by using an ac ammeter to measure the current.

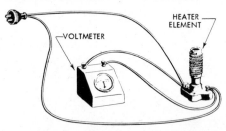

◆ **48. Current Used by Heater Element**

3. Determining the Wattage of a Household Appliance.

Materials needed are an ac voltmeter, ac ammeter, attachment plug, insulated wire, outlet box, and some type of household appliance such as waffle iron, toaster, heater, radio, or flat iron.

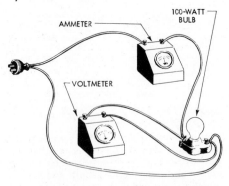

◆ **47. Hot Resistance of Light Bulb**

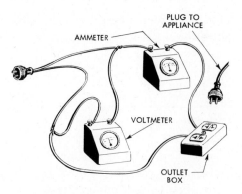

◆ **49. Wattage of an Appliance**

Wire a circuit as shown in Illustration 49. Plug the household appliance attachment plug into the outlet box. After measuring the voltage and the current use the watt formula to determine the wattage of the appliance.

4. Constructing a Soldering Iron.

Materials needed:

1 Wood handle (a file handle is satisfactory)
1 Piece of pipe (steel or brass), ½" outside diameter, 7" long
1 Piece of round copper rod, ½" x 1¾"
1 Heating element (Eagle soldering iron element Catalog No. 407, Eagle Electric Mfg. Co. Inc., 23-10 Bridge Plaza So., Long Island City 1, New York)
6' of No. 18 heater cord
1 Metal ring (diameter and width to fit handle)

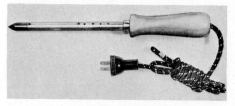

◆ **50. Electric Soldering Iron**

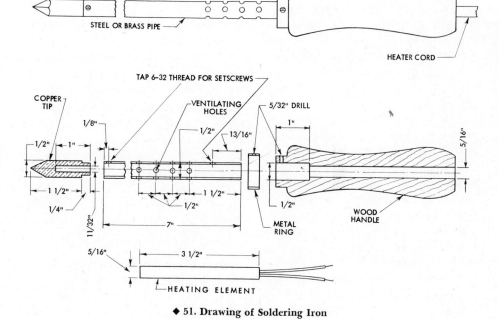

◆ **51. Drawing of Soldering Iron**

Drill the handle as shown in Drawing 51. Drill a series of $1/8''$ ventilating holes in pipe. Drill and tap 6–32 threads in each end of pipe for setscrews. Drill a $11/32''$ hole in one end of the copper rod $1''$ deep. File or turn shoulder on copper tip so that it will fit snugly into the pipe. File a four-sided point on the tip.

Insert the pipe into the handle and secure with the setscrew. Push heater cord through both the handle and the pipe. Connect the heating element leads to the heater cord extending out from the pipe. Solder and tape the connections. With the heater element extending $3/4''$ beyond the end of the pipe determine where the cord will enter the wood handle. At this point wrap the cord with several layers of tape so that the cord cannot be pulled out of the iron.

Place the tip in the pipe and secure with the setscrew. Drill $5/32''$ holes through the metal ring and into the handle. Slip the ring on the handle and fasten it in place with a round-head wood screw. Connect the attachment plug cap to the end of the cord. The iron is now ready to try out. Using an ac ammeter and a voltmeter determine how much wattage the iron is consuming.

REVIEW QUESTIONS

1. How can a knowledge of Ohm's law help us in making electrical calculations?

2. Explain what is meant by "hot" resistance in an electrical circuit.

3. How can we overcome the effect of high resistance in an electrical circuit?

4. If we increase the voltage in an electrical circuit containing a light bulb what might happen? Why?

5. Explain with a diagram how you would connect a voltmeter and an ammeter in a circuit to determine the "hot" resistance of a light bulb.

6. In what ways could you increase the amount of current flowing in an electrical circuit?

7. What are the three basic measurements usually made in an electrical circuit?

8. An electrical circuit has a voltage of 10 volts and the current flowing through it is 2 amperes. What is the resistance of the circuit?

9. Calculate the current flowing through a circuit that has a voltage of 50 volts and a resistance of 10 ohms.

10. If an electrical circuit has a resistance of 50 ohms and current of 3 amperes flowing through it, what is the voltage being applied to the current?

11. Name the unit used to express electrical power.

12. State the basic formula for calculating electrical power.

13. What is the unit used to measure the amount of electricity used?

14. How are home electric bills figured?

UNIT 14
CONNECTING ELECTRICAL CIRCUITS

Series Battery Connections

We know that a single dry cell will deliver 1½ volts and that one cell of a storage battery delivers about 2 volts. We also know that batteries, which are made up of more than one cell, deliver more voltage than a single cell. These batteries have the cells connected so that the voltage of all of the cells can be added together to make the total voltage of the battery.

When cells are connected so that the voltage or pressure is increased the cells are said to be connected in

series. In a series connection of cells the positive terminal of one cell is connected to the negative terminal of the next cell. In this way each cell adds its voltage to that of the other cells. The total voltage produced by all cells connected in series is equal to the sum of the voltages of all the cells. See Illustration 52.

When connecting cells in series it is important to watch the polarity of the cells so that the positive terminal of one cell always connects to the negative terminal of the next cell. The two remaining terminals, one positive and one negative, make up the total voltage of the battery and must not be connected together. These two terminals are connected across the

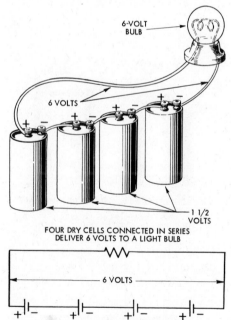

FOUR DRY CELLS CONNECTED IN SERIES
DELIVER 6 VOLTS TO A LIGHT BULB

♦ 52. The voltage of cells connected in series is found by adding the voltages of the individual cells.

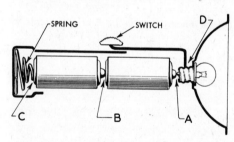

♦ 53. This flashlight uses two dry cells connected in series to produce 3 volts to light the bulb. The positive terminal of the first cell makes contact with the bulb at point *A*. Flashlight cells always use the bottom of the cell as the negative terminal. The negative terminal of the first cell connects to the positive terminal of the second cell at *B*. At *C* the negative terminal of the second cell makes contact with the spring attached to the frame of the flashlight. When the switch is closed the lead connected to the bulb at point *D* completes the circuit.

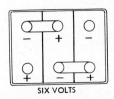

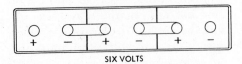

SIX VOLTS

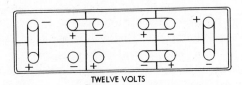

SIX VOLTS

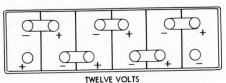

TWELVE VOLTS

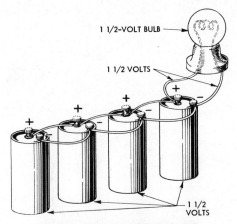

TWELVE VOLTS

From Automotive Electrical Systems,
American Technical Society

◆ 54. These are typical cell arrangements for automobile storage batteries.

electrical device called the electrical *load*.

Six-volt storage batteries have three 2-volt cells connected in series. Storage batteries producing 12 volts have six cells connected in series. See Illustration 54. Radio B batteries that deliver 45 volts have 30 dry cells connected in series, each delivering 1½ volts.

Parallel Battery Connections

Dry cells which are very small will not last as long as dry cells which are

larger. Even though the voltage of the two cells is the same the large cell will be able to deliver more current.

Sometimes the cells or batteries that are available are not large enough to supply the amount of current needed in a circuit. When this happens the cells or batteries can be connected together so that they each help provide current for the circuit.

Cells are said to be connected in *parallel* (Illustration 55) when they help each other by providing an increase in the amount of current available. When connecting cells in parallel the negative terminals of all the cells are connected together and all

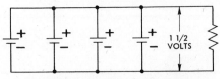

FOUR DRY CELLS CONNECTED IN PARALLEL DELIVER 1 1/2 VOLTS TO A LIGHT BULB. THE FOUR CELLS CAN PRODUCE FOUR TIMES THE CURRENT OF A SINGLE CELL.

SCHEMATIC DIAGRAM OF FOUR CELLS IN PARALLEL CONNECTED TO A LOAD

◆ 55. Current capacity is increased when cells are connected in parallel.

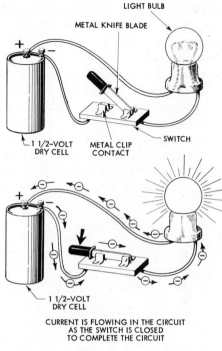

LIGHT BULB

METAL KNIFE BLADE

1 1/2-VOLT DRY CELL   METAL CLIP CONTACT   SWITCH

1 1/2-VOLT DRY CELL

CURRENT IS FLOWING IN THE CIRCUIT
AS THE SWITCH IS CLOSED
TO COMPLETE THE CIRCUIT

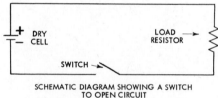

+ DRY CELL   LOAD RESISTOR

SWITCH

SCHEMATIC DIAGRAM SHOWING A SWITCH
TO OPEN CIRCUIT

◆ 56. A switch enables us to start and stop
the flow of current.

Opening and Closing Circuits

When two wires are connected to the terminals of a dry cell and then connected to a light bulb the light will burn. The light can be turned off by disconnecting one wire from either of the battery terminals or from either of the connections to the lamp socket. When the light is burning this is called a complete or *closed circuit* and when one of the wires is disconnected the current stops and it is called an *open circuit.*

Practically every circuit needs some method of opening and closing. When the circuit is closed electrons start to flow and electricity is able to do its work. When the circuit is open the electrons are no longer flowing. The device used to open and close circuits is called a *switch*.

The switch is always placed in one side of the line so that the circuit can

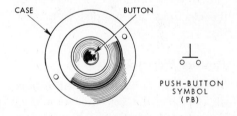

CASE   BUTTON

PUSH-BUTTON
SYMBOL
(PB)

the positive terminals are connected together. Each cell delivers current to the circuit without an increase in the voltage.

If batteries are not large enough to provide the amount of current needed they too may be connected in parallel. When batteries are connected in parallel it is necessary that each of them deliver the same voltage.

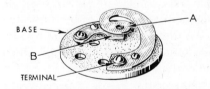

BASE   A

B

TERMINAL

◆ 57. A push button is used as a switch when
the circuit needs to be closed for very short
intervals. When the button is pushed, contact
A touches contact *B*, making a complete
circuit.

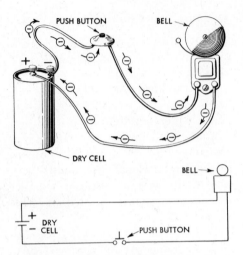

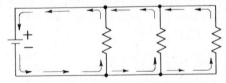

♦ 58. The push button closes the circuit, allowing current to flow from the cell to the bell.

be opened or closed. As the switch is closed the two contacts in the switch come together and the electrons flow through the switch to the rest of the circuit. Opening the switch breaks the contact points on the switch and the electrons are stopped from flowing.

Parallel Electrical Circuits

If we wish to have three bulbs burn off the same dry cell they should be connected directly across the two terminals as shown in Illustration 59. These bulbs are said to be connected in parallel because each bulb provides a separate parallel path through which the current must flow.

The parallel circuit is probably the most common type of circuit and is used in the wiring of all circuits for the home. Each electrical device in a

parallel circuit is connected directly across the two wires used to carry the current flow. All devices must have the same voltage rating as the full voltage of the source of electricity that is connected to them.

In parallel circuits, each device provides a separate electron path and each path may have a different amount of current flowing through it. The amount of current flowing through each path is determined by the resist-

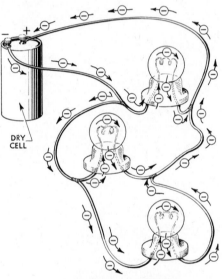

THREE BULBS CONNECTED IN PARALLEL. ARROWS SHOW THREE SEPARATE PATHS FOR CURRENT FLOW.

SCHEMATIC DIAGRAM OF THREE BULBS IN PARALLEL

♦ 59. The voltage across each bulb connected in parallel is the same as that of the source of electricity.

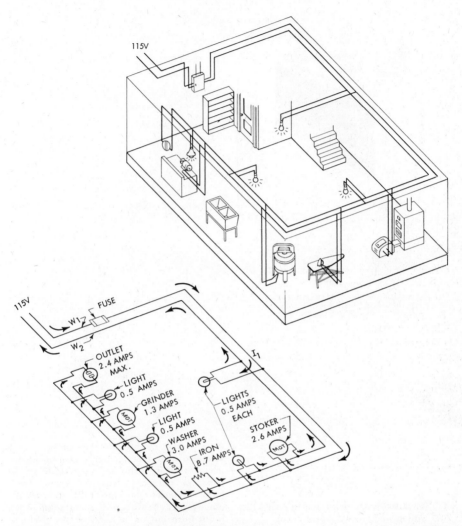

◆ 60. **The wiring installed in the basement of this home is a practical example of parallel circuits.**

ance of the device since the voltage across every item is the same. Through the use of parallel circuits it is possible to have a separate switch on each appliance so that they can be turned on or off individually.

Series Electrical Circuits

If a 6-volt storage battery is to be connected to a light bulb that is made for 3 volts it would be necessary to reduce the voltage going to the bulb. Some method must be used to use up

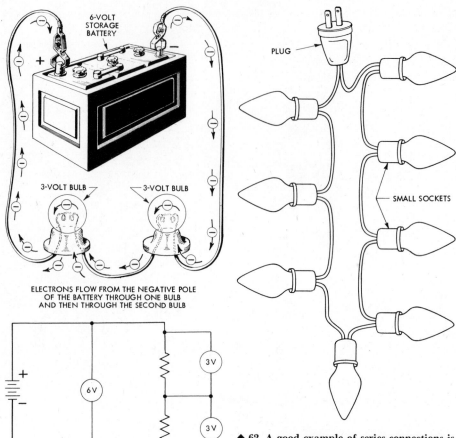

6-VOLT
STORAGE
BATTERY

3-VOLT BULB   3-VOLT BULB

ELECTRONS FLOW FROM THE NEGATIVE POLE
OF THE BATTERY THROUGH ONE BULB
AND THEN THROUGH THE SECOND BULB

3 V

6 V

3 V

SCHEMATIC DIAGRAM SHOWING HOW VOLTAGE
IS DIVIDED ACROSS EACH BULB

◆ 61. When bulbs are connected in series, the voltage is divided between them.

PLUG

SMALL SOCKETS

◆ 62. A good example of series connections is found in some types of lights used on Christmas trees. The bulbs are each made for 15 volts. By connecting eight of these 15-volt bulbs in series, the entire 120 volts of the home outlet circuit is used. Should one of the bulbs burn out or be removed the circuit is opened and the string of lights will not burn.

the extra 3 volts delivered by the battery. By connecting another 3-volt bulb so that the electrons will flow through both bulbs, the 6 volts of the battery would then be divided between the two bulbs. Thus each bulb would be using 3 volts from the battery. These two bulbs that have the same

electron flow through them are said to be connected in *series*.

In a series circuit the electrons must flow through each device before the circuit is completed. If a number of devices are connected in series the voltage is divided among them. Should any device be disconnected from a series circuit the entire electron flow is stopped.

Some small radio receivers often called ac-dc receivers also have the radio tube filaments connected in series. When one of the tubes burns out it is necessary to test all of the tubes to determine which one must be replaced to get the set back into operation.

Calculating Resistance

The formulas used in calculating the total resistance in series, parallel, and series-parallel circuits are given on pages 236-237.

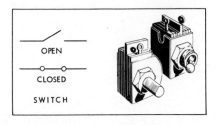

This is how the basic switch symbols are to be drawn.

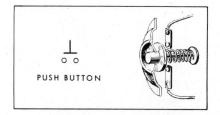

This is the symbol for the common spring-return push button.

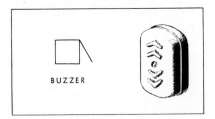

The buzzer may be identified by adding the abbreviation AC or DC within the square.

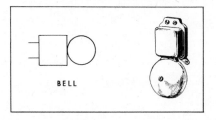

This symbol is used for the familiar call bell.

INTERESTING THINGS TO DO

◆ 63. Push Button

1. Constructing a Push Button.
Material needed:

2 Pieces of soft pine, $\frac{1}{4}$" x $1\frac{1}{2}$" x $1\frac{1}{2}$"
1 Piece of $\frac{3}{8}$" dowel, $\frac{1}{2}$" long
2 Pieces of 26 gage spring brass, $\frac{1}{4}$" x $1\frac{1}{4}$"
4 Wood screws, brass roundhead (RH),
   $\frac{1}{4}$", No. 2
2 Fahnestock clips, small (not essential)

Drill a $\frac{3}{8}$" hole in the center of the block to be used for the top. Refer to Drawing 64. Use a round file to ream

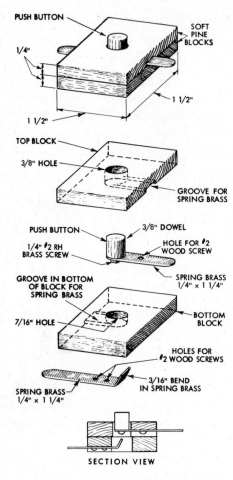

PUSH BUTTON

SOFT PINE BLOCKS

1/4"

1 1/2"

1 1/2"

TOP BLOCK

3/8" HOLE

GROOVE FOR SPRING BRASS

PUSH BUTTON

3/8" DOWEL

1/4" #2 RH BRASS SCREW

HOLE FOR #2 WOOD SCREW

GROOVE IN BOTTOM OF BLOCK FOR SPRING BRASS

SPRING BRASS 1/4" x 1 1/4"

7/16" HOLE

BOTTOM BLOCK

HOLES FOR #2 WOOD SCREWS

3/16" BEND IN SPRING BRASS

SPRING BRASS 1/4" x 1 1/4"

SECTION VIEW

◆ **64. Push Button Construction**

the hole so that the $\frac{3}{8}''$ dowel will fit loosely into the hole.

In one of the spring brass strips drill a hole large enough for a No. 2 wood screw $\frac{3}{16}''$ from one end. A second hole should be drilled in the center of the brass strip. Fasten the dowel push button with a No. 2 brass screw to the strip as shown in the drawing.

Cut or file a $\frac{1}{4}''$-wide groove in the block to be used for the top. This

groove should allow the spring brass strip to fit level with the block when the dowel is placed through the hole. Fasten the strip to the block with a wood screw.

The block to be used for the bottom needs a $\frac{7}{16}''$ hole drilled in the center of it. A $\frac{1}{4}''$-wide groove should be cut or filed in this block so that the brass strip will fit into it. This groove will need to be deep enough to allow the wood screws which hold the strip in place to be level with the bottom of the block.

Bend the brass strip for the bottom. Form the contact at a 60° angle about $\frac{3}{16}''$ from the end. Place the strip in the groove in the block, holding the bent end so that it extends through the hole in the block. Mark where two holes are to be drilled into the strip so that it can be fastened to the block. Drill the holes in the brass strip large enough for a No. 2 wood screw.

Place the top and bottom blocks together and check to see that the spring contact does not touch the brass screw connected to the push button. These two points should be about $\frac{1}{16}''$ apart. If the spring touches the screw it will be necessary to cut or file about $\frac{1}{16}''$ off the spring contact.

After the contacts have been checked the bottom spring should be fastened to the block with wood screws. The top and bottom blocks may be glued together. The push button is completed and when the button is pressed it will now make contact with the bottom spring. If desired Fahnestock clips can be soldered on each end of the brass strips extending out of the push button.

◆ **65. Buzzer**

2. Constructing a Buzzer.
Material needed:

1 Wood base, 1/2″ x 2½″ x 2½″
1 Piece soft steel, round, 1/4″ x 1 1/16″
2 Fiber washers, 1/8″ x 3/4″
1 Piece of spring brass, 26 gage, 7/8″ x 1 1/4″
1 Piece of soft steel, round, 1/4″ diameter,
  1/8″ thick
1 Piece of 20 gage sheet steel, 7/8″ x 7/8″
20′ of No. 22 magnet wire
1 Piece of tin 3/4″ wide by 2″ long
2 Terminal screws

Bevel edges of block as shown in Drawing 66. Drill 1/4″ holes in the center of the washers. Drill two 1/16″ holes in one of the washers. One of the holes should be near the inside edge of the

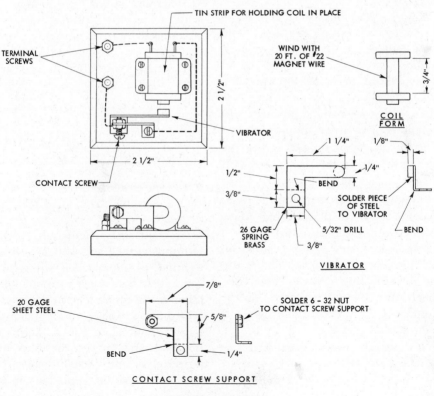

◆ **66. Buzzer Details**

washer and the other hole near the outside edge. Place the washers on each end of the ¼″ steel rod so that they will be ¾″ apart. Insert one end of the magnet wire through the inside hole in one of the washers allowing about 3″ to extend beyond the washer. Wind eight layers of wire evenly on the steel core. The remaining end of the wire should then be pulled through the outside hole in the washer.

Cut the piece of spring brass to the shape shown in the drawing. This spring is the vibrator of the buzzer. Drill and bend the spring brass as shown in the drawing. Solder the small piece of ¼″ round steel to the vibrator.

Cut the piece of sheet steel to shape as illustrated in the drawing. Bend and drill this contact screw support. Solder a 6–32 brass nut to this support. File a blunt point on the end of a roundhead brass 6–32 machine screw. This will serve as the adjusting screw in the contact screw support.

Drill two holes at each end of the tin strap. Shape this strap so that it will hold the coil in place.

Mount all of the parts on the wood base as shown in the drawing. Make connections on the bottom of the wood block as indicated by dotted lines on the drawing. Place a 6–32 brass nut on the adjusting screw and insert the screw into the nut soldered on the contact screw support. The buzzer is now ready to test.

Connect the two terminal screws to 3 to 6 volts either ac or dc. Adjust the contact screw to the desired tone.

◆ 67. **Push Button and Buzzer Connected to a Battery**

3. Connecting Dry Cells in Series to Operate a Buzzer.

Obtain four dry cells, a buzzer, a push button, and some wire for connections. Connect the dry cells in series as described in the text so that the center or positive terminal of one cell is connected to the outside or negative terminal of the next cell. See Diagram 68. When all of the cells have

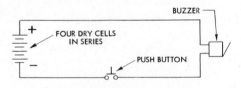

◆ 68. **Connecting Dry Cells in Series to Operate a Buzzer**

been connected together, a positive terminal of one cell and a negative terminal of another cell will be unconnected. Run a wire from one of those terminals to a terminal on the push button. Connect the other push button terminal to one of the buzzer terminals and connect the other buzzer terminal to the remaining dry cell terminal. Press the push button and if all connections have been made correctly the buzzer will operate.

When making an electrical connection by attaching a wire to a terminal screw, always wind the wire around the terminal in a clockwise direction. See Illustration 69. This will cause

◆ 69. **Wind Wire Clockwise around a Terminal**

the wire to wrap more closely around the terminal screw and prevent a loose connection.

When the buzzer is operating, note the loudness of the sound produced by the four dry cells connected in series. The tone of a buzzer may be changed by adjusting the contact screw. If it does not have an adjustable contact screw, the fixed contact arm may be bent backward or forward to produce the same result.

4. Connecting Dry Cells in Parallel to Operate a Buzzer.

Connect the four negative terminals of the dry cells together. Connect the four positive terminals of the dry cells

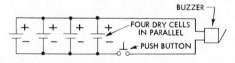

◆ 70. **Dry Cells in Parallel to Operate a Buzzer**

together as shown in Diagram 70. Connect a wire from the negative terminal of one of the end cells to a push but-

ton terminal. Connect a wire from the other push button terminal to one of the buzzer terminals. Connect a wire from the other buzzer terminal to the positive terminal of the end cell. Press the push button and if all connections have been made correctly the buzzer will operate. Is the sound of the buzzer louder or softer than with the series connection? Why?

5. Connecting Dry Cells in Series with Light Bulbs in Parallel.

Obtain four dry cells, four 6-volt flashlight bulbs, four miniature receptacles, a single-pole switch, and some wire for connections. Connect the four dry cells in series. Connect the receptacles together by placing them in line and running a wire to each terminal on the same side as shown in Diagram 71. Connect the opposite sides of the

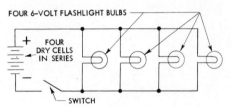

◆ 71. **Dry Cells in Series with Light Bulbs in Parallel**

receptacles in the same manner. Connect a wire from the unconnected positive terminal of the dry cells to one of the receptacles. Connect the other terminal of the same receptacle to one of the switch terminals. Connect the other switch terminal to the negative terminal of the dry cell. Close the switch and if all connections have been made correctly, the light bulbs should light.

Unscrew one of the bulbs and notice whether the remaining bulbs get dimmer or brighter. Normally, when good dry cells are being used there will be no change in the brightness of the bulbs. When the dry cells are nearly worn out they cannot supply sufficient voltage to force the correct amount of current through the light bulbs. When one of the bulbs is removed from the parallel circuit the remaining bulbs are apt to burn brighter, because they will require less current from the dry cells.

6. Connecting Dry Cells and Flashlight Bulbs in Series.

Obtain four dry cells, four 1.5-volt flashlight bulbs, four miniature receptacles, a single-pole switch, and connecting wire. Connect four dry cells in series. Connect the four receptacles in series, as shown in Diagram 72. Run

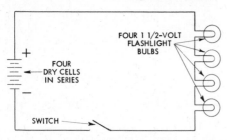

♦ **72. Dry Cells and Flashlight Bulbs in Series**

connecting wires between the dry cells, receptacles, and switch so that they will all be in series. Close the switch and if all connections have been made correctly the bulbs will light. Unscrew one of the light bulbs. What happens? Where could this system of connections be used? Replace the 1.5-volt flashlight bulbs with 6-volt bulbs. What happens? Why?

7. Connecting Dry Cells in Series with Push Buttons and Buzzers in Parallel.

Obtain four dry cells, two push buttons, two buzzers, and connecting wire. When you worked with dry cells and buzzers before, you learned that increasing the number of dry cells caused the buzzer to make a louder sound. Although most buzzers will operate on voltage as low as 1.5, when they are used in noisy locations for signaling, a higher voltage is used. The circuit you are about to connect is like the ones used where it is necessary to operate two buzzers from two push buttons which are located at different points.

Connect four dry cells in series. Connect the two push buttons in parallel and the two buzzers in parallel as shown in Diagram 73. Connect one of

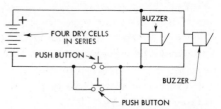

♦ **73. Dry Cells in Series with Push Buttons and Buzzers in Parallel**

the series dry cell terminals to one of the buzzer terminals. Connect the other buzzer terminal to one of the push button terminals. Connect the other push button terminal to the remaining series dry cell terminal. Press either push button and if the connections have been made correctly, both buzzers should operate. Place your hand against the armature of one of the buzzers, so that it will not operate and press a push button. Is the operation of the other buzzer affected? Why?

8. Connecting a Three-Wire Return Call Buzzer System.

Obtain four dry cells, two push buttons, two buzzers, and connecting wire. Connect the dry cells in series. Cut two pieces of wire the same length several feet long. Connect one end of each wire to a buzzer. Connect the other end of each wire to a push button. Arrange the wires so that a buzzer and a push button will be at the same ends of the wires. See Diagram 74. Connect a short piece of wire between the buzzer and the push button at both ends of the longer wire. Connect one terminal of the dry cells to the short piece of wire that connects a push button and a buzzer. Connect another wire from the remaining terminal of the dry cells to the short piece of wire that connects

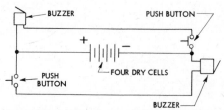

◆ 74. Three-Wire Return Call Buzzer System

the other push button and buzzer together. The connections should appear as shown in the diagram. If the connections have been made correctly a buzzer at the opposite end will sound when either push button is pressed. Draw a diagram showing how the system could be made to operate using four wires between the stations. What is the advantage of the three-wire system? Where could such a system be used?

REVIEW QUESTIONS

1. Draw a diagram showing how you would connect a group of dry cells to provide 7½ volts.

2. If we connect two No. 6 dry cells in series with two small flashlight cells, what voltage will we obtain?

3. List as many applications of cells connected in series as you can.

4. When would you connect dry cells in parallel?

5. Draw a diagram showing how you would connect four 1½-volt flashlight bulbs to a 6-volt storage battery.

6. Name as many applications of light bulbs connected in series as you can.

7. What is the disadvantage of connecting light bulbs in series?

8. Are the light bulbs in your home connected in series or in parallel?

9. What is the difference between a "short" circuit and an "open" circuit?

10. Make a list of the different types of switches that you know about.

Electricity

for

Everyday Living

〰〰〰〰〰〰〰〰〰〰〰〰〰〰〰〰〰〰〰〰〰〰〰〰

UNIT 15
GENERATION AND TRANSMISSION OF ELECTRICITY

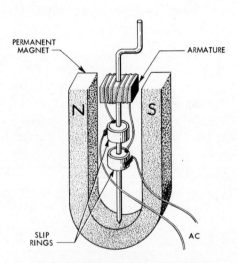

PERMANENT MAGNET

ARMATURE

N S

SLIP RINGS

AC

◆ 1. This illustration shows the fundamental parts of an alternating current generator.

Generating Electricity

We learned in Unit 7 that electricity could be generated when a coil of wire is rotated in a magnetic field. We also found that generators can be used to deliver either alternating current or direct current. An alternating current generator uses slip rings to deliver electricity to the brushes and direct current generators use a commutator. See Illustrations 1 and 2.

Most commercial alternating current generators used to provide electricity for the home produce a 60-cycle alternating current. This means that the direction of current flow is changing 120 times every second.

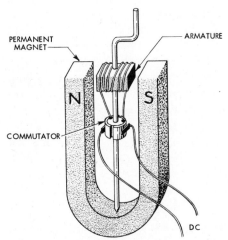

PERMANENT MAGNET

ARMATURE

N

S

COMMUTATOR

DC

◆ 2. A direct current generator has these basic parts.

Rotating Generators

Every generator needs some method of rotating the armature or rotor. The large generators used to produce electricity for towns and industry are usually rotated by water power or by steam. These huge generators weighing many tons need a tremendous amount of power to turn them over.

The armature or rotor of these generators is usually coupled to a turbine. See Photograph 3.

A *turbine* is a device that might be compared to a windmill. A windmill has several blades or vanes that are pushed by the wind. As the blades rotate the center shaft connected to the blades turns so that it can be used to pump water or turn other devices.

When water power is used to turn over a generator it is necessary to have a rapid flow of water. This can be accomplished by a large waterfall such as the Niagara Falls or by having a dam that holds back a huge lake of water. As the water goes over the falls or out through the bottom of the dam it flows through a water turbine. This turbine has vanes called *blades* (or *buckets*) against which the water flows. The force of the water turns the turbine and the turbine rotates the generator.

Steam pressure is used to turn turbines on many commercial generators.

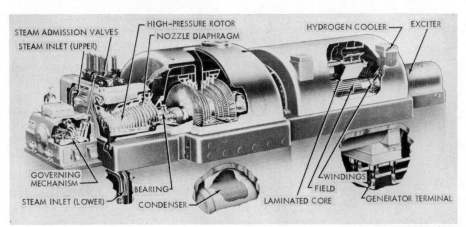

STEAM ADMISSION VALVES
STEAM INLET (UPPER)
HIGH-PRESSURE ROTOR
NOZZLE DIAPHRAGM
HYDROGEN COOLER
EXCITER
GOVERNING MECHANISM
BEARING
STEAM INLET (LOWER)
CONDENSER
LAMINATED CORE
WINDINGS
FIELD
GENERATOR TERMINAL

Courtesy General Electric Co.

◆ 3. In a modern turbine generator, the steam pushes against many blades to turn the rotor.

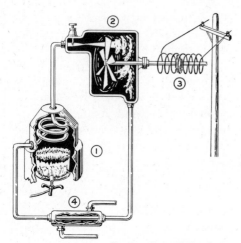

Courtesy General Electric Co.

◆ 4. How a steam turbine rotates a generator: 1. Steam is generated in a boiler. 2. Steam passes through a nozzle striking turbine blades. Blade wheel rotates. 3. Turbine turns rotor of generator and electricity is generated. 4. Exhaust steam from turbine is condensed and returned to boiler.

High-pressure steam is directed against the blades on a turbine at the rate of about 1,200 miles per hour. These steam turbines have a series of blade wheels arranged so that steam must pass through from 17 to 20 turbine wheels. The steam passes through the

nozzle and strikes a row of blades on the first wheel, it loses some of its pressure, and then passes into another set of nozzles, then through another row of blades, and so on down the line. Sometimes the wheel that holds the last set of blades is 12′ in diameter.

A large volume of water is needed for both the water turbine and the steam turbine. For this reason most commercial generating plants are located near lakes or other places where water is readily available.

Rotating Small Generators

Generators used to produce electricity where commercial electricity is not available usually are rotated by a diesel engine. Some small generators use a windmill to turn them over.

Large amounts of direct current are often needed for such purposes as electroplating and arc welding. These gen-

◆ 5. An old-type hand-operated generator used to ring telephone bells. Five horseshoe magnets were used to produce the magnetic field.

Courtesy Wincharger Corp.

◆ 6. A gasoline engine driven generator. The 10,000-watt generator will deliver either 115 volts or 230 volts.

◆ 7. A diesel-electric power unit. The 60,000-watt generator will deliver either 115 or 230 volts alternating current.

erators are usually rotated by electric motors. When an electric motor is used with a generator to produce electricity the combination is called a *motor-generator* (Photograph 8).

Transmission Line Losses

Commercial generating plants must be able to deliver tremendous amounts of electricity to serve the entire needs of a town or city. These generating plants sometimes supply electricity for several communities and often must be located many miles away from where the electricity is used. Power lines called *transmission lines* carry the electricity from the power plant to the towns.

The voltage of these transmission

◆ 8. A motor-generator set using an electric motor to rotate the generator.

◆ 9. This small dynamotor is a combination motor and generator. It was used to provide power for radio equipment in a Navy airplane.

lines is usually very high. Voltages of 66,000 to 110,000 volts are very common. High voltages are used for two reasons: (1) to reduce the voltage loss that would result from the resistance of the wire; (2) to reduce the amount of heat that would result from the large amount of current that would have to flow in the wire.

◆ 10. Large water-driven generators used by the Bureau of Reclamation on the Coulee Dam in the State of Washington.

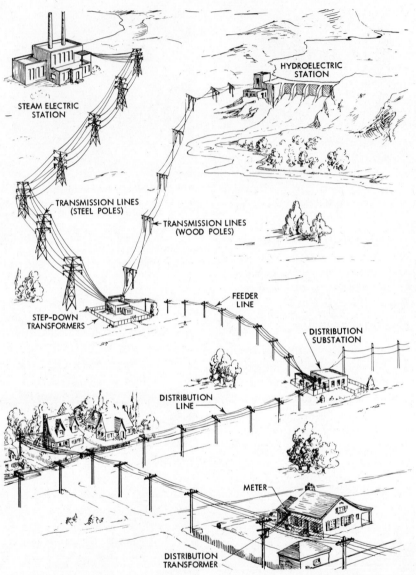

♦ 11. This drawing shows how electricity might be produced and delivered to a city. A steam generating plant and a water power generator both produce electricity. After stepping up the voltage at both plants, the transmission lines deliver this very high voltage to a central station. Here the electrical power from each plant is brought together. Large step-down transformers reduce the voltage, for safer handling, as the electricity nears the city. The feeder lines deliver the electricity to a distribution substation where the voltage is again reduced. From this substation the distribution lines take the electricity to the homes.

287 KV LINES

LIGHTNING ARRESTERS

CRANE

TRANSFORMER

SPARE

Courtesy Westinghouse Electric Corp.

◆ 12. Transmission lines deliver 287,000 volts to this substation. These large transformers reduce the voltage before the electricity is sent on to other distribution stations.

Loss Due to Resistance

We know that the circuits used in most homes are 115 volts. If the generator located many miles away from the homes delivered 115 volts to the transmission lines there would be a very large loss in voltage by the time it reached the homes. It would take several times the 115 volts to leave the generator so that the correct voltage would be available when it reached the town. The loss would be due to the resistance of the many miles of wire used to carry the electricity. To overcome this loss caused by the wire resistance, it is customary to use high voltages so that plenty of voltage will be available when the electricity reaches its destination.

Heavy Current Flow

If the generator produced only 115 volts of electricity the amount of current needed to supply all of the homes in a community would be very high. The amount of current would be so great that it would be impossible to build a generator with large enough wire to handle the current flow. It would be very difficult to have transmission wires large enough to take care of the current needs. By using high voltages it is possible to reduce the amount of current in the circuit.

We learned that electrical power

Courtesy General Electric Co.

◆ 13. Steel tower supporting electric transmission lines.

was made up of the voltage multiplied by the current. From this we can see that large quantities of power can be made available if we have: (1) large voltage and a low current; or (2) a low voltage and a high current. Since high current would make the wire heat up it is necessary to reduce the current flow. Transmission lines must have a low current flow and a very high voltage.

Using High-Voltage Transmission Lines

Some commercial generators develop alternating current voltages up to 12,500 volts and higher. Even this is not enough to use on transmission lines that are hundreds of miles long. Voltages are stepped up to 66,000 or even higher after leaving the generator. A special device called a *transformer* is necessary to step up the voltage. We shall learn how transformers function in the next unit.

After the voltage has been stepped up it is carried by the transmission lines to local distributing stations called *substations*. There the voltage is reduced. The amount of voltage reduction varies according to the needs. Voltages of 2,200 volts to 6,000 volts are very common in substations.

From the substation the electricity is carried by power lines to the various sections of the community. Before bringing the electricity into the home it is necessary to again step the voltage down. Transformers located on top of power poles reduce the voltage to 115 or 230 volts. These 115- or 230-volt lines are then brought into the home.

Transmission Line Construction

High-voltage transmission lines are made of several strands of heavy wire. Stranded wire makes the cable flexible so that it can swing between the poles without breaking. Also it makes it possible to coil the cable for easy handling. These cables use several strands of either copper or aluminum wire. Sometimes a kind of hollow tubing is used for transmission lines instead of solid wire. The hollow tubing makes a stronger cable than a solid wire of the same weight. The outside diameter of the entire cable may be as large as 2".

Transmission poles are made of either steel or wood. Often the wire on top of the poles is a ground wire that serves as protection for the transmission wires in the event lightning strikes. If lightning strikes it usually hits the highest point. Since the ground wire is higher than the other wires the lightning is shorted to the ground.

Because of the extreme high voltage on transmission lines, it is necessary to use large insulators on the arms of the poles. These insulators prevent the electricity from shorting between the wires or from shorting to the power pole.

REVIEW QUESTIONS

1. What is the main difference between an alternating current generator and a direct current generator?

2. How are large commercial generators usually rotated?

3. What is the purpose of a turbine?

4. What effect do large transmission lines have on the voltage?

5. Why is it necessary to have a high voltage and a low current on transmission lines?

6. Give two reasons why high voltages are used on transmission lines.

7. What electrical measurements are needed to determine the electrical power in a circuit?

8. Name the device used to step up the voltage after it has been developed by a generator.

9. After delivering the electricity by a transmission line to a city why is it necessary to reduce the voltage?

10. What is the purpose of the ground wire on top of transmission poles?

UNIT 16

USING TRANSFORMERS TO INCREASE AND DECREASE VOLTAGE

Inducing Current in a Coil

We know that if a bar magnet is pushed into the center of a coil that electricity will be induced in the coil. Electricity can be induced only when the magnet is moving. This induced current was alternating current since each time the magnet was pushed in or out of the coil the direction of current flow changed.

Expanding and Collapsing of the Lines of Force

A magnetic field that is starting or stopping makes the lines of force build

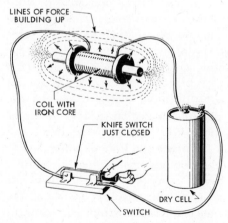

◆ **14. As switch is closed the magnetic field expands.**

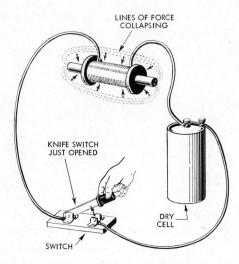

◆ 15. As switch is opened the magnetic field collapses.

up and then collapse around a coil. In Illustration 14 when the switch is first closed the lines of force build up or expand all around the coil. In just a fraction of a second all of the lines of force will have been completed and the coil becomes an electromagnet. When the switch is opened as in Illustration 15 the magnetic field starts to collapse. When all of the lines of force are gone the coil is no longer an electromagnet. Each time the switch is closed the lines of force build up and each time the switch is opened the lines of force collapse. The closing of the switch completes the circuit and at this time the lines of force start to move out all around the coil forming a path from one pole to the other. Just as soon as the circuit is opened all the lines of force start to move back toward the coil until they disappear.

Inducing Current in a Coil by the Current in Another Coil

A second coil is now placed near the first coil as shown in Illustration 16. The leads of this coil are connected to a galvanometer. When the switch is closed the galvanometer needle moves in one direction and then returns to the zero position. As long as the switch remains closed the galvanometer needle remains at zero. As soon as the switch is opened the needle moves in the opposite direction and then returns to zero as shown in Illustration 17.

From this we can see that current is induced in the second coil each time the switch is opened or closed. This is exactly the same as when a bar magnet is moving in or out of a coil. As long as the magnet is moving, current is induced in the coil.

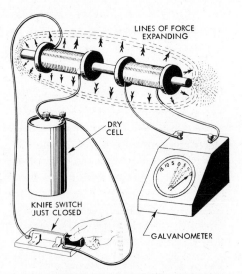

◆ 16. Galvanometer connected to the secondary coil shows that current is induced by the primary coil when the switch is first closed.

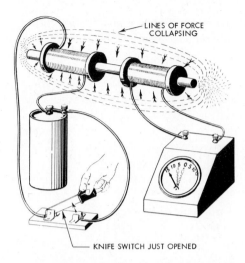

◆ 17. When the current in the primary coil is stopped, the collapsing line of force induces a current in the secondary coil. The galvanometer shows that the current in the secondary coil flows in a direction opposite to that in which it flowed when the switch was closed.

Illustrations 16 and 17 show that current can be induced in a coil by current in another coil. To induce current it is necessary to stop and start the current in the first coil. When the current is started by closing the switch the magnetic lines of force start building up and move so that they cut through the second coil. As soon as all of the lines of force have been completed, the magnetic field is not moving and current is no longer induced in the second coil. When the switch is opened the lines of force start to collapse and again current is induced in the other coil. As soon as all of the lines of force collapse current stops flowing. Since the current flows first in one direction and then the other direction, the induced current is alternating current.

Transformer Operation

Having one coil induce a current in another coil is the principle of the *transformer*. The first coil is called the *primary* winding. It must have a current that is starting and stopping to induce a current in the second coil. The second coil is called the *secondary* winding.

To improve the operation of a transformer the two windings are placed over a soft iron core as shown in Photograph 18. The iron core pro-

◆ 18. An iron core placed in the center of the primary coil and the secondary coil will improve the efficiency of the transformer.

vides a much better path for the magnetic lines of force to flow through. It also concentrates the lines of force so that they do not spread out but remain close to the coils of wire. By concentrating the lines of force the efficiency of the transformer is greatly improved. Most transformer cores are made of many soft iron strips called *laminations* (Illustration 19). These laminations help in improving the operation of the transformer.

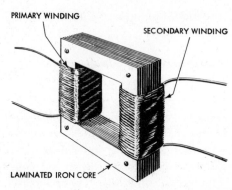

PRIMARY WINDING

SECONDARY WINDING

LAMINATED IRON CORE

◆ **19. A drawing showing the construction of a transformer. The closed iron core provides a path for the magnetic field to flow through. The laminated core made of thin strips of soft iron improves its efficiency.**

Using Transformers on Alternating Current

We have just learned that a transformer consists of a primary winding and a secondary winding surrounding an iron core. We also know that to induce a current in the secondary winding it is necessary to have the current in the primary continually starting and stopping.

A type of current that is continually starting and stopping by changing the direction of electron flow is alternating current. When alternating current is connected to the primary of a transformer the magnetic field will be expanding and collapsing each time the current starts and stops. This will induce a current in the secondary winding which will also be alternating current.

When direct current is connected to the primary of a transformer it is necessary to have some type of switch that will continually open and close the circuit to induce a current in the secondary winding.

Step-up Transformers

In the study of commercial generators we found that they produce alternating current. We also learned that it was necessary to step up the voltage of these generators so that high voltages would be available for the transmission lines. Transformers are used to step up the voltage. Generating plants use alternating current because the primary of the transformer can be connected directly to the output of the generator.

A transformer is a *step-up transformer* if the secondary winding has more turns than the primary winding. If the secondary has more turns than the primary, the lines of force cut through more turns of wire and the voltage is increased. In a transformer that has 100 turns of wire on the primary and 200 turns of wire on the secondary, the voltage across the secondary will be twice as much as the voltage connected to the primary. The relationship between the number of

Courtesy General Electric Co.
◆ **20. Large transformers are used in a power substation.**

turns on a primary winding to the number on the secondary is often referred to as the *ratio* between them. In the transformer shown in Illustration 21, there is a 1 to 2 ratio.

Step-up transformers are used wherever it is necessary to increase the voltage. It is possible to increase the voltage a little or a great deal, depending upon the need. When it is desired to step up the voltage from 10 volts to 100 volts then the secondary winding must have ten times as many turns as the primary. Of course, there is some loss in a transformer. To take care of this loss a few extra turns of wire must be added to the secondary winding.

Step-down Transformers

After the high-voltage transmission lines bring the electricity into a town or city, a substation is used to reduce the voltage. These substations use *step-down transformers* to lower the voltage so that it will be safer to handle.

In a step-down transformer the primary has more turns than the secondary. Since the secondary winding has fewer turns than the primary winding the lines of force are cutting through fewer turns and the voltage is reduced.

If we wish to obtain 10 volts from a 100-volt alternating current source of electricity a transformer can be used. The secondary would have one-tenth as many turns as the primary. See Illustration 22.

Other Uses of Transformers

Transformers have many uses. All types of transformers are in use in the home and in industry. It is possible to have more than one secondary winding

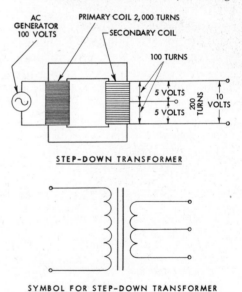

PRIMARY COIL
100 TURNS

SECONDARY COIL
200 TURNS

100
VOLTS
AC

AC GENERATOR
50 VOLTS

STEP-UP TRANSFORMER

IRON CORE

PRIMARY

SECONDARY

SYMBOL FOR STEP-UP TRANSFORMER

◆ 21. A step-up transformer increases voltage.

AC
GENERATOR
100 VOLTS

PRIMARY COIL 2,000 TURNS

SECONDARY COIL

100 TURNS

5 VOLTS

5 VOLTS

200 TURNS

10 VOLTS

STEP-DOWN TRANSFORMER

SYMBOL FOR STEP-DOWN TRANSFORMER

◆ 22. The voltage from a step-down transformer may be divided as needed.

♦ 23. A small step-down transformer is shown on the left. The iron laminations and the primary and secondary coils are shown on the right.

on a transformer. For example, in many radio receivers a single transformer steps up the voltage to 300 volts with one set of windings and another winding steps the voltage down to 6 volts. The secondary can have as many different windings as necessary to step the voltage either up or down.

Train transformers used to run toy trains step down the 115 volts ac to from 5 to 25 volts. This lower voltage is connected to the train tracks and makes it safe to handle all parts of the circuit. Door chimes and door bells require a low voltage and transformers are used to step down the 115 volts to between 10 and 20 volts. Television sets use transformers in many ways. In one circuit of a television set the voltage is stepped up by a transformer to as high as 20,000 volts.

INTERESTING THINGS TO DO

1. Making a Transformer.

Materials needed:

1 Wood base, ½" x 3" x 5"
1 Piece cardboard, fiber, or plastic tubing, 1" diameter, 1¾" long
2 Fiber or masonite washers, ⅛" thick, 1¾" outside diameter
85' Soft iron wire, 16, 18, or 20 gage (Cut approximately 200 pieces 5" long)

1 Spool magnet wire, No. 32, enamel-covered
1 Spool magnet wire, No. 24, enamel-covered
2' Stranded radio hook-up wire
1 Piece sheet steel, 20 gage, ½" x 3"
1 Piece sheet steel, 20 gage, 1¼" x 6"
2 Terminal screws

The transformer you are about to make has an output of 12 volts and will operate any of the projects described in this book that are intended to work on alternating current.

Make a winding form for the transformer by making holes in the center of the fiber or masonite washers large enough to make a snug fit on the ends of the 1″ tubing. See Drawing 25. Glue the washers to the tubing and drill a ³⁄₃₂″ hole through one of the washers close to the tubing. Cut a piece of

◆ 24. Step-Down Transformer

radio hook-up wire 6″ long and insert one end of it through the hole in the fiber or masonite washer. Solder one

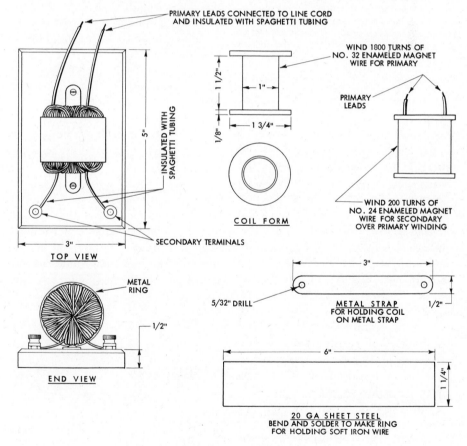

◆ 25. Drawing of the Step-Down Transformer

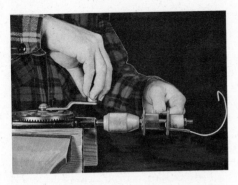

◆ 26. Using a hand drill clamped in a vise to wind the transformer. A long bolt holds the coil form. One end of the bolt is tightened in the chuck of the hand drill. It is necessary to determine how many revolutions the chuck makes for each revolution of the handle. One hand of the operator feeds the wire on the form while the other hand turns the drill handle.

end of the hook-up wire to the end of the spool of No. 32 magnet wire. Wrap the soldered joint with a piece of Scotch electrical tape and proceed to wind 1,800 turns of wire between the two washers. See Photograph 26. Wind the wire on the form as evenly as possible and when the winding is completed, carefully drill another 3/32" hole through the washer, close to the winding. Cut another piece of radio hook-up wire 6" long and insert one end of it through the hole in the washer. Solder the hook-up wire to the end of the completed winding and insulate the joint with a piece of electrical tape. Wrap the winding with a layer of thin cardboard. This completes the primary winding.

Drill two 3/32" holes through the fiber or masonite washer, opposite to the ones drilled previously. One of the holes should be drilled close to the

cardboard wrapping and the other near the outside edge of the washer. Cut a piece of radio hook-up wire 6" long and insert one end of it through the inner hole in the washer. Solder the hook-up wire to the end of a spool of No. 24 magnet wire, wrap the joint with a piece of tape and proceed to wind 200 turns of wire over the cardboard wrapping. Insert another 6" piece of radio hook-up wire through the outer hole in the washer and solder it to the end of the No. 24 magnet wire. Insulate the joint with a piece of tape. Wrap the winding with several layers of thin cardboard. This completes the secondary winding.

Fill the center of the winding form with pieces of the 5" soft iron wire, allowing an equal amount of wire to extend from each end of the form, as shown in Photograph 27. Force extra pieces of wire through the center of the form, so that all of the iron wires will be held firmly in place. Bend each piece of iron around the coil form and cut the ends off so that they overlap about 1/2" on the outside of the form. Slip short pieces of radio spaghetti tubing over the coil leads when the iron wires are being bent around coil form

◆ 27. The wire core is placed in the center of the coil form. Ends of the wires are bent so that they touch each other.

to protect the insulated covering on the leads. Make a ring to fit snugly around the transformer with the 1¼″ x 6″ piece of sheet steel and force it over the steel wires surrounding the coils. Drill and shape the ½″ x 3″ piece of sheet steel as shown in the drawing and solder it to the metal ring. This piece will serve to secure the transformer to the wood base. Place two terminal screws at one end of the wood base and secure the transformer to the base, so that the secondary leads are at the same ends as the terminal screws. Secure the leads to the terminal screws. Connect an attachment plug cap, or a piece of lamp cord and a plug cap, to the primary terminals. The transformer is now ready for its initial tryout.

2. Making a Shocking Coil.
Materials needed:

1 Wood base, ½″ x 2½″ x 2¾″
2 Fiber washers, ⅛″ thick, ¾″ diameter
1 Piece soft steel rod, round, ¼″ diameter, 1⅜″ long
15′ Magnet wire, No. 24, enamel-covered
1 Spool magnet wire, No. 34, enamel-covered
2 Pieces spring brass, 26 gage, ½″ x 1⅜″
1 Piece spring brass, 26 gage, ¼″ x 1⅝″
1 Piece tin, 1″ x 2½″
2 Terminal screws
2 Pieces flexible radio hook-up wire
2 Pieces brass or steel tubing, ½″ x 3″
1 Flashlight cell, size C

Place the fiber washers on the ends of the steel rod with one end extending ⅛″ beyond the face of the washer. Drill two holes in one washer near the steel core for the primary coil leads. Pass one end of the No. 24 magnet wire through one of the holes and let about 4″ of wire extend beyond the washer.

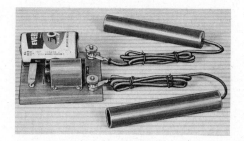

◆ 28. A Shocking Coil

Wind four layers of wire on the steel core and pass the other end of the wire through the remaining hole in the fiber washer. Wrap a layer of paper around the primary coil and drill two small holes in the other washer for the secondary coil leads. One hole should be drilled close to layer of paper and the other near the outer edge of the fiber washer. Secure the end of the steel core that extends beyond the fiber washer in the chuck of a hand drill and place the hand drill in a vise between two pieces of wood. Insert one end of the No. 34 magnet wire through the inner hole in the fiber washer and wind the wire onto the space between the washers. Insert the end of the secondary winding through the outer hole in the fiber washer. Wrap a layer of thin cardboard around the completed coil. Cut, drill, and shape the piece of tin to serve as a strap for the completed coil and secure the coil to the wood base with small wood screws. Drill and bend the two pieces of spring brass to serve as flashlight cell holders, as shown in the drawing. Make a recess in one of the pieces of spring brass so that the positive or center post of the cell will fit into it. Secure the cell

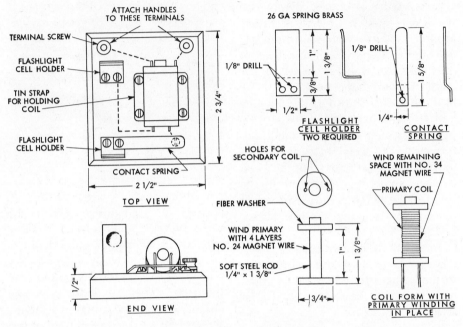

◆ 29. Drawing of the Shocking Coil

holders to the wood base, so that it will hold the cell tightly in place. Secure the contact spring to the wood base with one of the screws that hold the flashlight cell holder, as shown in the drawing. Place terminal screws in the wood base and connect the secondary coil leads to them on the bottom side of the base, as shown by the broken line. Make the other connections as shown. The pieces of tubing are to serve as handles. Any other size of tub-

ing may be used, but make certain there are no sharp or rough edges on the tubing which might cut the hands. Solder the ends of the flexible wire to the pieces of tubing and connect the other ends of the wire to the secondary coil terminals. The coil is now ready to operate. Pass the handles to your victim and close the contact spring. A quick, momentary contact does the trick.

REVIEW QUESTIONS

1. How is current induced in a coil by means of a bar magnet?

2. Explain what happens to the lines of force around a coil when the current in the coil is started and stopped.

3. What is necessary to induce a cur-

rent in one coil by means of current in another coil?

4. Name the two windings of a transformer.

5. What type of current is always produced in the secondary coil of a transformer?

6. What type of current is necessary in the primary winding of a transformer to induce a current in the secondary winding?

7. What is the difference between a step-up transformer and a step-down transformer?

8. If a step-up transformer has 400 turns on the primary winding and 1,200 turns on the secondary winding how much will this transformer increase the voltage?

9. Name several uses for step-down transformers.

10. What is the purpose of the iron core in a transformer?

UNIT 17
PROTECTING HOME ELECTRICAL CIRCUITS

Electrical Power Leads into the Home

At the local substation electricity is reduced to a fairly low voltage for distribution around the city. Voltages are usually 2,400 volts or higher on the power poles going to the residential areas. Before the electricity is brought into the home the voltage must again be reduced. A transformer called a *pole transformer* usually mounted on top of a power pole is used for this purpose. The pole transformer in Illustration 30 provides the electricity for several homes and reduces the voltage to either 115 volts or 230 volts.

When 115 volts is brought into the home it requires two wires and this is called a *two-wire service.* The use of 230-volt service in the home is becoming more common all the time and is called a *three-wire service.* In a three-wire service one wire is called the *neutral wire.* Illustration 30 shows how it is possible to obtain 115 by connecting to the neutral wire and to either of the other wires. The 230 volts, used on water heaters and electric ranges, is available from the other two leads.

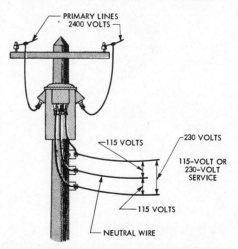

♦ 30. A pole transformer steps down the voltage before it reaches the home. By using the two outside wires, 230 volts is available. For 115 volts, one of the outside wires and the center neutral wire are used.

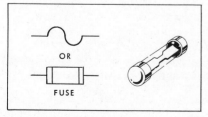

The top symbol can be used for any fusible element.

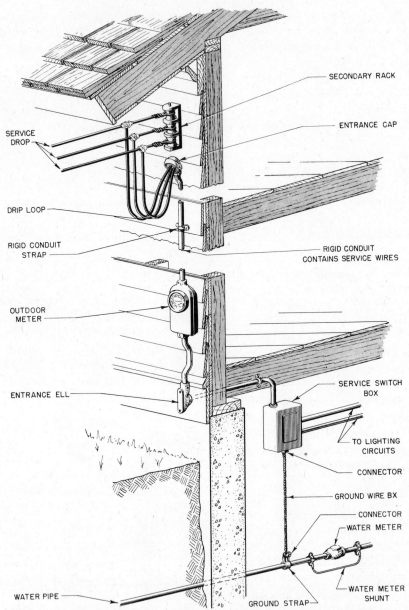

SECONDARY RACK

ENTRANCE CAP

SERVICE DROP

DRIP LOOP

RIGID CONDUIT STRAP

RIGID CONDUIT CONTAINS SERVICE WIRES

OUTDOOR METER

ENTRANCE ELL

SERVICE SWITCH BOX

TO LIGHTING CIRCUITS

CONNECTOR

GROUND WIRE BX

CONNECTOR

WATER METER

WATER METER SHUNT

WATER PIPE

GROUND STRAP

◆ 31. **The principal parts of a typical house wiring system are shown in the above illustration. Local electrical codes may require different locations for these service connections.**

The power service leads going into the home are connected to a kilowatt-hour meter that keeps a record of the quantity of electricity used by the home. This meter was discussed in Unit 13.

Distributing the Electricity

After going through the meter, the electricity is connected to a *distribution panel*. This panel is a box that contains the switches used to turn off the electricity in the house and it also encloses the safety devices used to protect the various circuits in the home. Either fuses or circuit breakers are used to safeguard the electrical circuits. They open the circuit and stop the flow of electricity whenever too much current starts to flow. If too much current is allowed to flow, the wires in the house could get hot and start a fire.

These safety devices protect the circuit against "short circuits" and from overloads. Short circuits often occur when the insulation covering the wires connected to an electrical appliance such as a floor lamp becomes worn. The broken insulation allows the wires to touch each other and the result is a short circuit if the lamp is plugged into the house outlet. To prevent a fire from starting the safety device immediately opens the circuit and stops the electricity from flowing. After the cord has been repaired the fuse can be replaced or the circuit breaker reset.

If too many electrical appliances are plugged into a single electrical circuit the quantity of current needed to operate the appliances could very easily cause heating in the house wiring. This is prevented through the use of protective devices that open the circuit.

In the home there are usually from three to six branch circuits. Each branch circuit has a separate fuse or

◆ 32. Three of the fuses are cartridge-type fuses. The fuse on the right is a plug fuse.

circuit breaker. When branch circuits are used, an overload or a short circuit stops the electricity from flowing in only one part of the house. The rest of the circuits may be used until the defect has been repaired.

Fuses as a Safety Device

Fuses are of two types, the *plug fuse* and the *cartridge fuse*. See Photograph 32. The plug fuse is the most common type of fuse found in the home where 115 volts is used. Cartridge fuses are used where heavy current is needed and on circuits using 230 volts or more.

The important part of the fuse is the thin strip of metal, usually zinc, that will melt when the current flow becomes too great (Illustration 33).

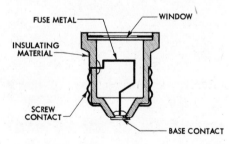

◆ 33. Construction of the plug fuse that is used in homes.

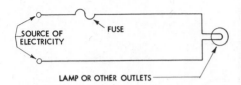

SOURCE OF ELECTRICITY — FUSE — LAMP OR OTHER OUTLETS

◆ **34.** A fuse is connected in series or in one line of the circuit the same as a switch is connected in the circuit. The entire current from the circuit flows through the fuse. If the current flow is greater than the rating of the fuse it will "blow" and the circuit is opened.

◆ **35.** A good fuse and a burned-out fuse. Fuses are enclosed in a case to make them safe to screw in and also to prevent the hot metal from scattering when the fuse "blows."

The size of the zinc strip is selected according to the number of amperes of current which it will carry without melting. Each fuse is marked to indicate the amount of current it will handle before it "blows."

◆ **36.** Placing a fuse in the type of fuse box found in most homes.

◆ **37.** Cartridge-type fuses are used in this box, which has a switch that disconnects all circuits.

Most branch circuits in the home use a 15-ampere plug-type fuse. It is important to use only 15-ampere fuses in these circuits. If larger fuses are installed the wire of the circuit can be overloaded and a fire could result from the heat developed in the wire.

Using Circuit Breakers To Protect Circuits

The type of circuit protection that is commonly used in new homes is called a *circuit breaker* (Photograph 38). It automatically turns off the cur-

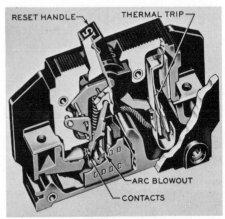

RESET HANDLE — THERMAL TRIP — ARC BLOWOUT — CONTACTS

Courtesy Federal Electric Products Co.

◆ **38.** Cutaway view of a circuit breaker unit.

rent when too many amperes flow in the circuit. The circuit breaker is a combination switch and safety device. When the switch is turned to the "on" position the circuit breaker contacts are closed. If a short or overload occurs the breaker opens the circuit. After the short has been repaired or the load cut down the breaker can be reset by turning the switch to the "off" position and then back to the "on" position.

The use of circuit breakers eliminates hunting for a fuse and also prevents a careless person from installing a large fuse that could overload the circuit. Circuit breakers are labeled, the same as fuses, with their current-carrying capacity.

There are two types of circuit break-

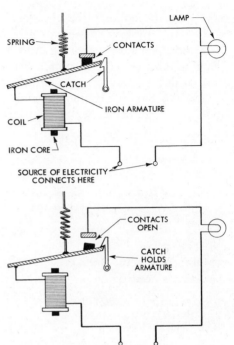

◆ **40. These drawings show the construction of a magnetic circuit breaker. The coil has all of the current from the circuit flowing through it. When the breaker is set the contact points are closed and the circuit is complete. If too much current flows through the circuit the coil pulls the iron armature down, opening the contact points. The catch holds the armature from moving upward to close the contact points again.**

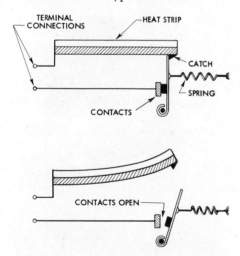

◆ **39. These drawings show the construction of a heat strip circuit breaker. When the heat strip is cool, the catch holds the contact points together. If too much current flows through the terminal connections, the heat strip expands and bends upward. The catch releases the arm and the spring opens the contact points. To use the breaker again it must be reset so that the contact points are closed.**

ers—the heat strip breaker and the magnetic breaker.

Heat Strip Breaker

The *heat strip breaker* uses a strip made of two different kinds of metal either welded or riveted together. When too much current flows through the strip the metals get hot. The heat makes the metals expand but, since they are two different kinds of metal, one expands more than the other. Since the lower metal strip expands more than the upper piece, the heat strip curves upward. This bending of the heater strip allows a spring in the switch to open the contact points. See Illustration 39. The amount of current necessary to open the contact depends upon the design of the heater strip.

The Magnetic Circuit Breaker

The *magnetic circuit breaker* uses an electromagnetic coil to open the circuit. See Illustration 40. A coil is connected in series with the circuit so that all of the current must pass through it. When the current becomes too great the magnetic pull of the coil moves the metal bar called the *armature* toward the coil. As the armature moves toward the coil it breaks the contact points and opens the circuit.

Both the heater strip breaker and the magnetic breaker must be reset by hand before the circuit is closed again.

INTERESTING THINGS TO DO

Making a Circuit Breaker.
Materials needed:

1 Piece of soft steel rod, ⅜" diameter, ⅛" thick
2 Pieces wood, ¼" x 3" x 5"
2 Fiber or masonite washers, 1" diameter
1 Piece fiber or cardboard tubing, 1/16" wall, ⅜" inside diameter, 1⅜" long
5' Soft iron wire, No. 18
1 Spool enamel-covered wire, No. 22
1 Piece sheet steel, ⅜" x 2¼", 20 gage, for contact arm
1 Piece sheet copper, ⅜" x ⅜", 20 gage, for contact on contact arm
1 Piece sheet steel, ⅜" x ½", 20 gage
1 Piece sheet copper, ⅜" x 1¼", 20 gage, for stationary contact
1 Piece sheet fiber, 1" wide, 2½" long, ⅛" thick, for reset lever
1 Piece sheet steel or brass, 1¼" x 3½", 22 gage, for holding coil in place
2 Terminal screws
Miscellaneous screws, nuts, and washers (see text)

This circuit breaker will take the place of a fuse by opening the circuit when the current exceeds the amount for which it is set. The breaker may be adjusted to operate on currents from 1 to 3 amperes and it is adjusted by moving the coil toward or away from

◆ 41. A Magnetic Circuit Breaker

the contact arm. As the coil is moved away from the contact arm, more cur-

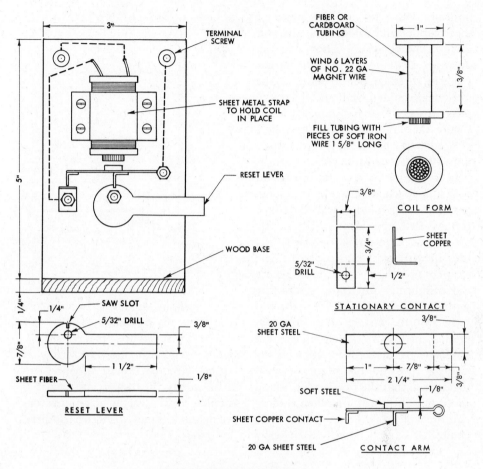

◆ **42. Drawing of Circuit Breaker**

rent will be needed to operate the breaker. Less current will be required as the coil is moved closer to the contact arm.

Make a coil form by drilling the fiber washers so that they will fit over the fiber tubing and glue one of them at each end of the tubing. Drill two small holes in one of the washers for the coil leads. Cut the piece of iron wire into short sections 1¾″ long and pack them into the center of the fiber tubing, as shown in the drawing. Wind the form with six layers of No. 22 magnet wire. Solder the piece of soft iron rod to the piece of sheet steel, 1″ from one end. Shape the opposite end to fit snugly around a 6–32 machine screw for the contact arm, as shown in the drawing. Bend the short piece of sheet steel and solder it to the contact arm opposite to the round piece of steel. This piece fits into the slot in the fiber reset lever when the arm is in the "on" position. Bend the smaller piece of sheet copper and solder it to the end of the contact arm, as shown in the drawing. Drill and shape the larger piece of sheet copper to serve as the stationary contact. Drill and shape the piece of sheet fiber for the reset lever. Secure the parts to one of the pieces of wood, as shown in the assembly drawing. The movable contact arm is held in line with the center of the coil with a 6–32 machine screw, 1¼″ long, hexagon nuts, and brass washers. Make certain that the arm swings freely on the machine screw, otherwise the breaker will not operate properly. The strap for holding the coil should secure the coil firmly when the screws are tightened, but it should allow the coil to be adjusted when two of the screws are loosened. Wire the circuit breaker as shown by the broken lines on the drawing. Join the two pieces of wood together so that the breaker will stand in an upright position. When the circuit breaker is being used it should be connected so that it will be in series

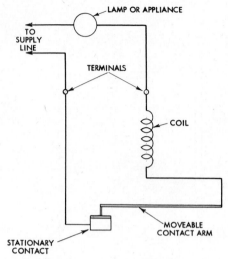

◆ 43. Circuit Breaker Diagram

with the lamp or device it is to control, as shown in Diagram 43.

While this circuit breaker was designed for low-voltage transformer or battery circuits, it will function satsatisfactorily on higher voltages if it is enclosed in a metal box to prevent accidental contact with current-carrying parts.

REVIEW QUESTIONS

1. What is the voltage of a three-wire service brought into a home?

2. What is the purpose of safety devices used in home wiring circuits?

3. Name two types of fuses.

4. Draw a diagram showing how fuses are connected in a lighting circuit.

5. What size fuse is used in most branch circuits in the home?

6. Name two types of circuit breakers.

7. How is a circuit breaker reset after it has opened the circuit?

8. Why is it important to locate the trouble in an electrical circuit before replacing a fuse or resetting a circuit breaker?

9. How is a heat strip constructed?

10. Explain how a magnetic circuit breaker operates.

11. What is the moving part of a magnetic circuit breaker called?

UNIT 18
ELECTRICAL WIRING IN THE HOME

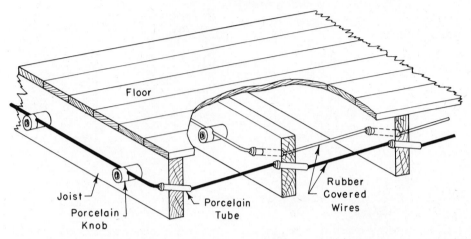

♦ 44. Concealed knob-and-tube wiring is one type of wiring system found in homes. Although formerly common, it is now prohibited in most localities.

Wiring Systems

Electrical circuits in most homes are connected to wall outlets, lights, and power outlets such as stoves and hot water heaters. Special protective covering must be provided for the wires that are used inside the walls, in the ceiling, and under the floor. Several systems are used to safeguard the wiring in the home. The main types of wiring are (1) knob-and-tube wiring, Illustration 44; (2) nonmetallic sheathed cable, Illustration 45; (3) armored cable, known as AC (also BX, which is a trade name), Photograph 46; and (4) electrical steel tube called conduit wiring, Illustration 47. Each locality has regulations regarding the type of wiring system that may be used.

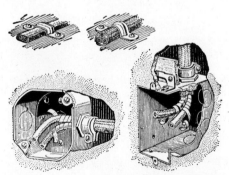

Courtesy General Cable Corp.

♦ 45. Method of fastening nonmetallic sheathed cable to floor joists and ceiling, and to switch and receptacle outlet boxes.

Courtesy Crescent Insulated Wire & Cable Co.

♦ 46. Armored cable is properly called "AC."

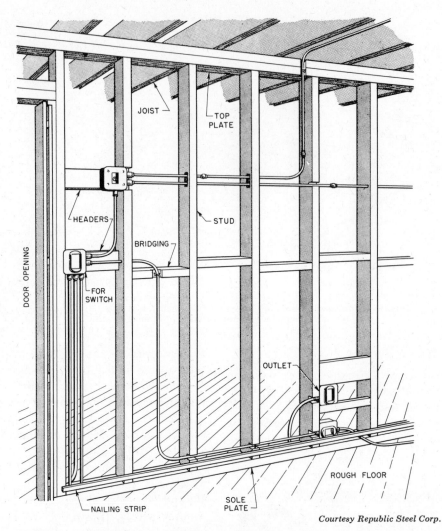

JOIST

TOP
PLATE

HEADERS

STUD

BRIDGING

DOOR OPENING

FOR
SWITCH

OUTLET

ROUGH FLOOR

NAILING STRIP

SOLE
PLATE

Courtesy Republic Steel Corp.

◆ **47. This illustration shows the installation of thin-wall steel tubing in a wood studding partition wall.**

Convenience Outlets

Wall outlets called *convenience outlets* are mounted in metal boxes called *outlet boxes*. The outlet is usually of the duplex type as shown in Illustra-

tion 48. Two wires carry the flow of electricity to the wall outlet. These wires start at the switch box where they are connected to a fuse or circuit breaker. Several outlets may be connected in parallel to the same pair of

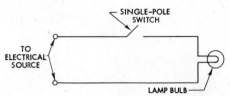

◆ 49. This is a wiring diagram using a single-pole switch.

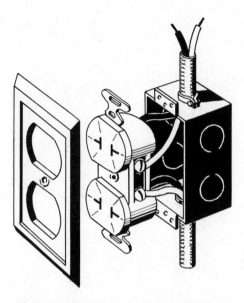

◆ 48. This is a duplex convenience outlet.

wires. Number 14 or 12 wire is usually used for convenience outlets.

Using Single-Pole Switches

In every lighting circuit it is necessary to be able to turn the lights on and off. Wall switches called *tumbler switches* are used for this purpose. The switch is always connected in one wire of the circuit as shown in Diagram 49. This is called a *single-pole switch*. A single-pole switch is one that has a single contact that can be opened and closed by pushing the tumbler either up or down. See Illustrations 50 and 52.

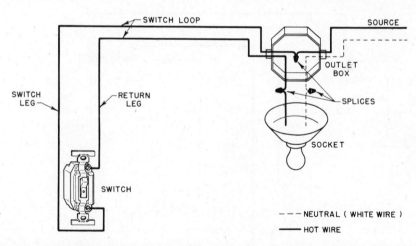

◆ 50. This illustration shows how the circuit in Diagram 49 would be connected when used in the home. All splices and connections are made inside of the boxes. Solderless connec-tors are used to join the wires together. The dotted line represents the neutral wire. This wire is usually solid white in color.

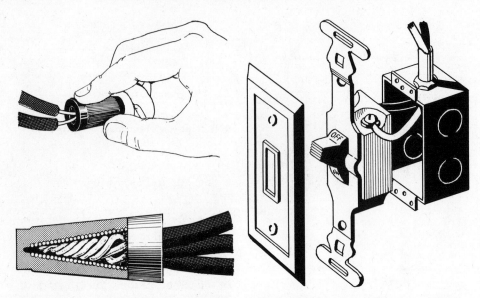

◆ **51. Solderless connectors often used for splicing purposes are screwed on to the splice. The cone-shaped spiral spring inside of the molded body presses the wires together, making solder unnecessary.**

◆ **52. Single-pole switch. To protect the switch it is placed inside of a metal box called a switch box. The front of the switch is covered with a switch plate, usually made of a plastic material.**

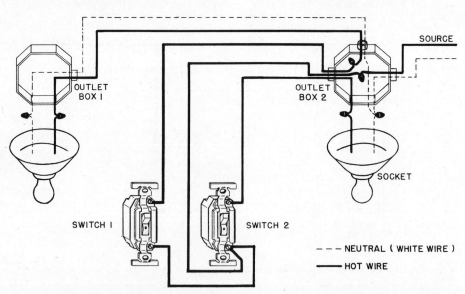

◆ **53. Two single-pole switches are sometimes placed side by side in the wall so that each can control separate lights in the room. Switch** No. 1 controls outlet box No. 1 and switch No. 2 controls outlet box No. 2.

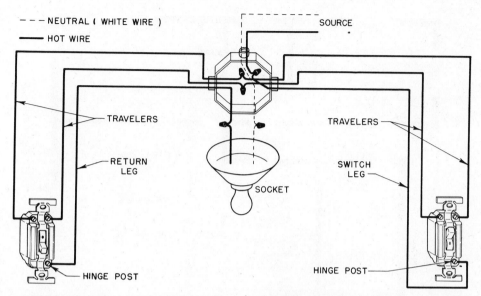

```
– – – NEUTRAL ( WHITE WIRE )                    SOURCE
——— HOT WIRE
```

TRAVELERS

TRAVELERS

RETURN LEG

SWITCH LEG

SOCKET

HINGE POST

HINGE POST

◆ 54. Two three-way switches can be used to control a single light from two different locations.

Using Three-Way Switches

Many times it is desirable to turn lights on and off from two different locations. A good example of this is found in a large room having a doorway at each end. A switch is placed near each entrance so that it is possible to turn the light on or off from either door. See Illustration 54. The controlling of lights from two separate locations is done through the use of two *three-way switches*. Three-way switches have three terminals for wire connec-tions instead of two terminals as found on single-pole switches. Diagrams 55 and 56 show the principle of operation of the three-way circuit.

Mercury Switches

The most common type of switch makes or breaks the contacts through the mechanical movement of the tumbler. This switch makes a distinct "click" each time it is opened or closed as the moving blade goes in or out of the contact points. A switch that is

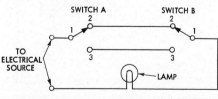

◆ 55. Two three-way switches controlling a single lamp. In this position the circuit is complete as switch *A* is in contact with terminal 2 the same as switch *B*.

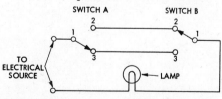

◆ 56. Switch *A* has been turned so that it is in contact with terminal *3*. This opens the circuit and the lamp is off. To turn the light on again switch *B* can be turned to terminal *3* or switch *A* must be turned back to terminal 2.

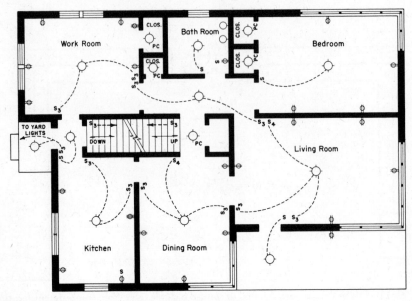

First Floor Plan

◆ 57. A blueprint of the first floor plan of a house showing the location of the various electrical outlets. Symbols are used for each of the outlets.

very desirable because of its silent operation is called a *mercury switch*. The mercury switch has a small quantity of liquid mercury that is moved against the contact points. Through the use of mercury it is possible to have a switch that does not "click" when it is turned on or off.

Reading Electrical Blueprints

When plans for homes are developed by an architect the placement of all of the electrical outlets, lights and other electrical connections are shown on the blueprints. Symbols are used to represent each of the electrical outlets.

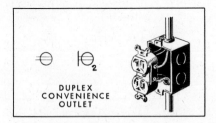

DUPLEX CONVENIENCE OUTLET

The duplex outlet is the standard kind and the small numeral "2" is generally not used with the symbol.

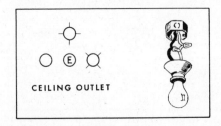

CEILING OUTLET

The circle at the left is the latest standard. The letter "E" may be used to prevent confusion with other kinds of symbols.

The letter "S" is the symbol for any single-pole switch.

The small "3" tells that the symbol is for a three-way switch.

INTERESTING THINGS TO DO

1. Connecting a Single-Pole Switch to a Light Socket.

Materials needed:

1 Light socket or receptacle
1 Fuse block
2 10-ampere fuse plugs
1 Single-pole switch
Connecting wire

Connect one terminal of the fuse block to one of the socket terminals. Connect a wire from the other socket terminal to a switch terminal. Connect the remaining switch terminal to the fuse block. The correct wiring is shown in Photograph 58. This is the type of circuit used to control a light when it is necessary to turn it on or off from only one location. Whenever a home or building has been wired properly, the wiring is so arranged that the neutral or grounded side of the lighting circuit is connected to the screw or shell terminal of the socket. This is done so that if one accidentally touches the base of a lamp while removing or replacing it and while standing on a damp floor, he will not receive a shock. With the help of your instructor trace the wiring in your school shop and wire the switch circuit so that it will follow the safety procedure outlined above.

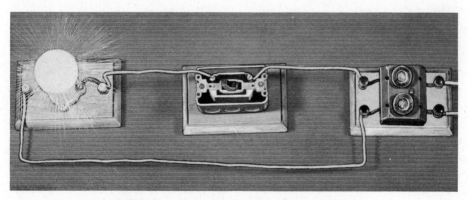

◆ 58. Using a Single-Pole Switch to Control a Light

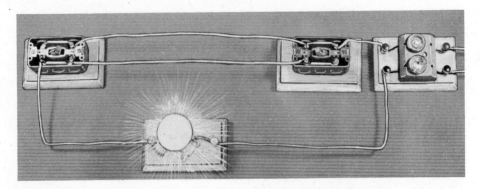

◆ 59. Using Two Three-Way Switches so that a Light Can Be Controlled from Two Locations

2. Connecting a Three-Way Switch.
Materials needed:

1 Light socket or receptacle
1 Fuse block
2 10-ampere fuse plugs
2 Three-way switches
   Connecting wire

A three-way switch is used when it is desired to turn a light on or off from two locations, such as the ends of a hall or the bottom and top landings of a stairway. A three-way switch has a single terminal at one end of the switch and two terminals at the opposite end. The single terminal is connected within the switch so that it makes contact with one of the other terminals at all times, whether the switch lever is in the up or down position.

Connect one terminal of the fuse block to one of the socket terminals. Connect the other socket terminal to the single terminal on one of the switches. Connect a wire from the remaining fuse block terminal to the single terminal on the other three-way switch. Connect the remaining two terminals on one switch to similar ter-

minals on the other switch. These connections between the two switches are generally referred to as *travelers*. Connect the fuse block to a 115-volt circuit and if all connections have been made properly the lamp may be turned on or off from either switch. The correct wiring is shown in Photograph 59.

3. Connecting a Four-Way Switch.
Materials needed:

1 Light Socket or receptacle
1 Fuse block
2 10-ampere fuse plugs
2 Three-way switches
1 Four-way switch
   Connecting wire

Wherever it is desired to turn a light or group of lights on or off from more than two locations, two three-way switches, together with one four-way switch for each additional control point, must be used. By adding one additional four-way switch to the circuit for each control point, the number of control points are unlimited. This type of switching circuit is very convenient for long hallways or stairways with a number of landings and makes it possible for a switch at any point to work independently of the other switches.

A four-way switch has two terminals at each end which are connected within the switch so that at either position of the switch arm, two terminals are connected directly across to the opposite terminals, or diagonally across to the opposite terminals. When you have finished wiring your circuit you may trace the path of current through the switch connections and see just how each switch can control the light independently of the other switches.

In wiring the four-way circuit the procedure for wiring the three-way circuit is followed, with the exception that a four-way switch is connected between the two wires that would normally connect the two three-way switches together. Connect the fuse block to a 115-volt circuit and if all connections have been made properly the lamp may be turned on or off with any of the switches. The correct wiring is shown in Photograph 60.

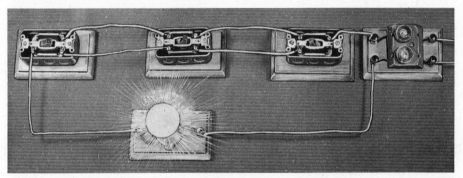

◆ 60. Connecting a Four-Way Switch Circuit so that a Light Can Be Controlled from Three Locations

REVIEW QUESTIONS

1. Name four types of wiring systems.

2. Why are protective coverings necessary for house wiring?

3. Give the common name used for wall outlets.

4. What size wire is usually used for wall outlets?

5. Draw a wiring diagram showing how a switch is connected in a circuit to turn a light off and on.

6. Why are convenience outlets and wall switches placed in metal boxes?

7. Draw a wiring diagram showing how two three-way switches are used to turn lights on and off from two locations.

8. Why are mercury switches used in some homes?

9. Draw a diagram of a room in your home, using symbols to show the location of convenience outlets, lights, and switches.

UNIT 19
TYPES OF LIGHTING

Incandescent Lamps Used To Produce Light

The incandescent lamp was mentioned in Unit 11. An incandescent lamp is one in which light is produced by the heating of a filament inside a glass bulb. Thomas Edison introduced the first practical incandescent lamp in 1879. Edison's lamp bulb contained a carbon filament sealed inside of an evacuated glass bulb (Illustration 61). All of the air had to be removed from the bulb to keep the carbon from burning up.

The modern incandescent lamp contains a spiral tungsten filament that will withstand very high temperatures. To prevent the tungsten from burning up, the oxygen is pumped out of the glass bulb. A small amount of argon and nitrogen gas is then put inside the bulb. This gas increases the light-producing ability of the bulb. Most incandescent lamps are designed to burn from 750 to 1,000 hours.

Shapes and Sizes of Incandescent Lamps

Incandescent lamps come in many shapes and sizes. The general-service type lamps used in the home range from 25 to 300 watts. The larger the wattage the greater the amount of electricity needed for operation of the lamp and the greater the output of light. These bulbs use what is known as a *medium screw-type base*. The glass may be either clear or inside-frosted. Inside-frosted is widely used as it reduces glare. Small lamps used for night lights and Christmas tree lights have either an *intermediate screw-type base*

CARBON FILAMENT

GLASS BULB

◆ 61. Edison's first electric lamp appeared in 1879.

INCANDESCENT LIGHT

This symbol is used for all incandescent-filament lights.

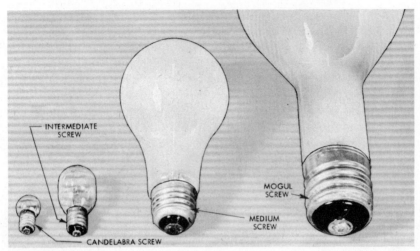

INTERMEDIATE SCREW

MOGUL SCREW

MEDIUM SCREW

CANDELABRA SCREW

◆ 62. Shown in this photograph are four sizes of screw-base type lamps commonly found in the home.

or a *candelabra base*. Lamps from 300 watts to 1,500 watts use a large base called a *mogul base*. See Photograph 62.

Three-Way Incandescent Lamps

Many table and floor lamps use a *three-way lamp*. This means that the lamp can produce three different amounts of light. They contain two filaments wired so that either may be used independently or the two filaments used in parallel so that both are on at the same time. See Illustration 63. These three-way lamps are usually 50-100-150–watt or 100-200-300–watt lamps. A three-way socket is used for these lamps and special three-way type switches are required to turn on each of the filaments. For example, in the 50-100-150 bulb the switch in the first position turns on the 50-watt filament, in the second position it turns on the 100-watt filament, and in the third position both filaments are in use.

Fluorescent Lamps Used To Produce Light

Fluorescent lamps have become very popular as a means of lighting. This popularity is due to their ability to produce more light with less electricity than incandescent lamps and also fluorescent lamps will last a lot longer without burning out.

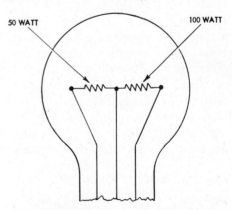

50 WATT   100 WATT

◆ 63. A three-light lamp contains two filaments. The switch is used to select either filament or both can be used at the same time.

The fluorescent lamp gives off light from an "electric discharge," or arc. An electric discharge can give off light just as lightning produces light when it discharges between the sky and the ground. In the fluorescent lamp an electric discharge is made to occur between the two ends of the sealed glass tube.

flow of electrons produces enough heat to vaporize the mercury. When current flows through a mercury vapor it produces a light called *ultraviolet light*. This ultraviolet is called *violet radiation* and is not a very bright light.

The inside of the fluorescent glass tube is coated with a very thin layer of powdered chemicals called *phosphors*.

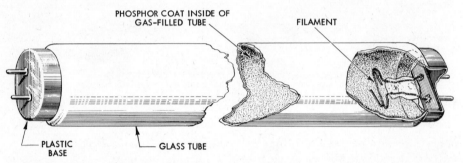

PHOSPHOR COAT INSIDE OF GAS-FILLED TUBE

FILAMENT

PLASTIC BASE

GLASS TUBE

◆ 64. Fluorescent lamps last longer than incandescent lamps and produce more light with less electricity.

Construction of the Fluorescent Lamp

A fluorescent lamp is made of a large glass tube that has had all of the air removed from it (Illustration 64). After the air has been removed a small amount of gas, such as argon gas, and a very small amount of mercury are placed inside of the tube. At each end of the glass tube is a small lamp filament that is called an *electrode*. These filaments are not intended to produce light but are made so that when they get hot they will throw off electrons. A special coating is placed on the filaments to give off the electrons. The electrons that are thrown off the filaments will flow through the argon gas from one electrode to the other. This

When the ultraviolet radiation from the mercury vapor hits the coating of phosphors it bursts into a brilliant glow of fluorescent light. The color of the light given off by the fluorescent coating depends upon the type of powder used.

The Starter Switch

The filaments at each end of the fluorescent tube are not needed once the flow of electrons has been started in the tube. After the arc between the two electrodes is started the current will continue to flow—as long as the circuit is completed. The filaments can be disconnected from the circuit as soon as the arc starts.

A switch called a *starter switch* is connected in series with the filaments

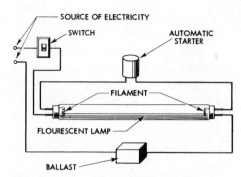

SOURCE OF ELECTRICITY
SWITCH
AUTOMATIC STARTER
FILAMENT
FLOURESCENT LAMP
BALLAST

◆ **65. The automatic starter is connected in series with the filaments of a fluorescent-tube circuit. As soon as the arc starts through the tube the starter automatically opens the filament circuit and the filaments are turned off.**

as shown in Illustration 65. As soon as the filaments become hot enough to give off electrons the starter switch is made to automatically open the filament circuit. These automatic starter switches are usually made of some type of bimetal strip that will open once the filaments become hot. The starter switch is mounted near one end of the tube so that it can easily be replaced if it becomes defective.

The Ballast

The arc in a fluorescent lamp will not start a flow of electrons unless there is a sudden high voltage produced between the two electrodes. It is necessary to get an electric arc to jump from the electrode at one end of the lamp to the electrode at the other end. To obtain this sudden high voltage a coil called a *ballast* is connected in series with the circuit, as shown in Illustration 66. The ballast is a coil of wire wound around an iron core.

When the fluorescent lamp is first

turned on the hot filaments give off electrons. At this time current is flowing through the ballast coil. Then the starting switch automatically opens. When this happens the magnetic field around the ballast coil suddenly collapses as the current momentarily stops. This sudden collapse of the magnetic field around the coil induces an instant high voltage in the ballast coil. This surge or "kick" of high voltage is strong enough to strike the arc across the lamp that starts the electron flow and lights the lamp.

The flow of electrons through the mercury vapor and the argon gas could easily become very great and burn out the lamp. Once the lamp starts it would draw more and more current. The ballast again goes into action since it is in series with the circuit. It performs like a resistor to keep the current from becoming too high. Here the ballast acts like a control valve and limits the amount of current flowing through the tube.

From this we can see that the ballast has two functions (1) to start the arc once the filament has started electrons

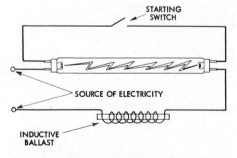

STARTING SWITCH
SOURCE OF ELECTRICITY
INDUCTIVE BALLAST

◆ **66. When the starting switch is opened the ballast produces a high-voltage surge that strikes the arc in the fluorescent tube.**

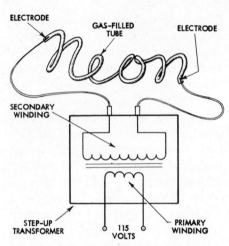

♦ 67. The high voltage of the transformer is connected to each end of the neon tube. The arc between the two electrodes lights up the sign.

to flow and (2) to protect the tube from having too much current flowing through it.

Neon Lamps

Most outdoor signs and advertising displays are lighted with neon lamps. Neon lamps consist of a glass tube with a terminal at each end. The tube is filled with neon gas. When a voltage is connected between the two terminals an electrical arc occurs, giving off a colored light. Pure neon gas gives off an orange color. To obtain additional colors other gases are added to the neon gas. Colors such as blue, green, red, yellow, and white are very common.

Some small neon tubes can be ignited with 115 volts. When large signs require longer neon tubes a higher voltage is necessary to light the tube. A step-up transformer is used to increase the voltage for the tube. See Illustration 67.

The longer the tube the higher the voltage must be stepped up. Step-up transformers with secondary voltages anywhere from 1,500 to 15,000 volts are used on neon signs. Since the neon lamp uses very little current, small wire can be used on the primary and secondary windings of the transformers.

INTERESTING THINGS TO DO

Making a Table Lamp.
Materials needed:

1 Piece wood, 1″ x 5″ x 8″
1 Piece wood, 1½″ x 3½″ x 8″
1 Threaded nipple, brass or steel, ⅛″ pipe size, 1″ long
1 Socket, brass, pull-chain, threaded cap
6′ Lamp cord, parallel, No. 18
1 Attachment plug cap

Make a ¼″ bevel along the upper edge of the piece of wood that is to be used for the lamp base. Starting at the center of one end of the base, drill a ⁵⁄₁₆″ hole lengthwise halfway through it. Drill another ⁵⁄₁₆″ hole through the base at a right angle to the first hole at the center, so that the two holes will meet. Beginning at the center of one end of the piece of wood that is to be used for the upright section, drill a ¹¹⁄₃₂″ hole lengthwise, half-way through it. Drill another ¹¹⁄₃₂″ hole through the other end of the wood block, so that the two holes meet. Screw the pipe nipple into one end of the

♦ 68. Table Lamp

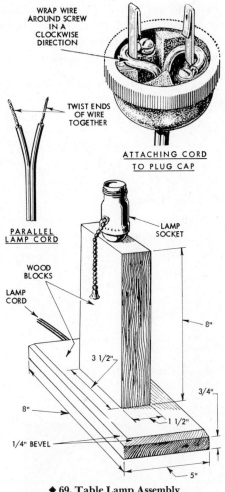

WRAP WIRE AROUND SCREW IN A CLOCKWISE DIRECTION

TWIST ENDS OF WIRE TOGETHER

ATTACHING CORD TO PLUG CAP

PARALLEL LAMP CORD

LAMP CORD

WOOD BLOCKS

LAMP SOCKET

8"

3 1/2"

3/4"

8"

1 1/2"

1/4" BEVEL

5"

♦ 69. Table Lamp Assembly

block so that only ¼″ extends above the wood. Secure the upright piece to the base with glue or wood screws as shown in Illustration 69. Insert the cord through the wood base and stand. Screw the socket cap to the nipple and connect the socket to the cord. Attach a plug cap to the other end of the lamp cord.

The lamp may be finished natural with clear shellac or lacquer, or painted to match any color scheme.

REVIEW QUESTIONS

1. Who introduced the first practical incandescent lamp?

2. What kind of filament is found in the modern incandescent lamp?

3. Why is it necessary to remove the oxygen from the glass bulb in an incandescent lamp?

4. Give the reason why some glass bulbs are frosted.

5. How many filaments are used in a three-way incandescent lamp?

6. What is the purpose of the filament in a fluorescent lamp?

7. Name the material that is used to

coat the inside of the glass tube of a fluorescent lamp.

8. What is the purpose of the automatic starter switch in a fluorescent lamp circuit?

9. How is the ballast used in a fluorescent lamp circuit?

10. Why is a step-up transformer used in a neon light circuit?

UNIT 20
HEATING WITH ELECTRICITY

Types of Heating Appliances for the Home

Many types of heating appliances are used around the home. Some of these are:

Toasters	Portable electric
Waffle irons	heaters
Electric flat iron	Electric blankets
Water heaters	Heating pads
Laundry dryers	Coffee makers
Electric wall heaters	Electric range
Electric ironer	

All of these heating appliances use a resistance wire to produce heat.

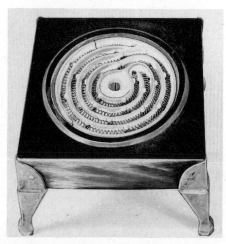

♦ 70. Spiral-type heating coil is used in this electric hot plate.

Nichrome wire, which is an alloy of nickel and chromium, is usually used as the heater wire. The wire is often wound in the form of a coil so that a long length of wire can be placed in a small space, as shown in Photograph 70. Sometimes a flat wire called *ribbon nichrome wire* (Photograph 71) is used for elements. All elements must be mounted in or on some type of insulating material. When the element is out in the open, such as in toasters and wall heaters, ceramic forms or mica sheets are used as the insulating material.

In addition to the open elements some elements called *calrod elements* are enclosed in a metal tube. See Photograph 72. The heating element is placed in the center of the hollow metal tube and an insulating material is packed in around it.

The element extends out each end of the tube and the ends of the tube are sealed so that air or moisture cannot get to the element. After the tube is sealed it is formed to the needed shape such as the spiral found in some electric ranges. In flat irons the calrod element is sometimes cast into the base of the iron (Illustration 73).

◆ 71. Flat wire called *ribbon nichrome* wire is usually used as the elements in electric toasters.

A hotter element can be produced by the calrod method since the element is placed much closer to where the heat is needed. Also there is no problem with air and moisture damaging the elements.

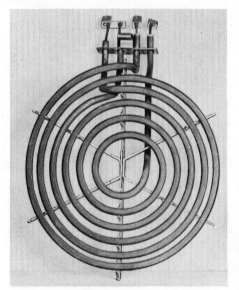

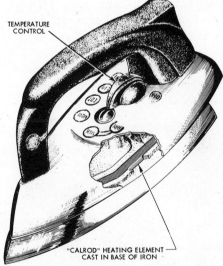

TEMPERATURE CONTROL

"CALROD" HEATING ELEMENT CAST IN BASE OF IRON

◆ 72. A heating element used in an electric stove. This unit has an element called a *calrod* inside of the spiral metal tube.

◆ 73. Automatic electric iron with temperature control. Heating element is cast in the base of the iron.

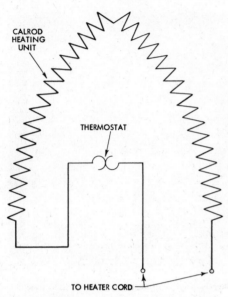

CALROD
HEATING
UNIT

THERMOSTAT

TO HEATER CORD

◆ 74. This is a wiring diagram of an electric iron.

Regulating the Heat

Appliances such as electric blankets, electric dryers, waffle irons, and flat irons use automatic heat regulators. These heat regulators, called *thermostats,* open and close the electrical circuit according to the selected temperature. Thermostats are usually made of bimetal strips that are placed inside of the heating unit. They operate like an automatic switch and are connected in series with the heater element.

As the element gets hot it gives off heat that warms the thermostat. Since the thermostat is made of a bimetal strip, the heat makes the strip expand and bend upward. When the temperature is great enough the strip opens the contact and opens the circuit. As the heater cools the temperature becomes lower and the bimetal strip bends back, closing the circuit so that the element again gives off heat.

Testing Heating Appliances

A simply constructed series lamp tester called a *continuity tester* can be used to check heating appliances. This tester consists of a cord with an attachment plug connected so that a 115-volt light bulb is in series with a pair of test leads. See Illustrations 75 and 76.

The attachment plug is plugged into a convenience outlet and when the two test leads are touched together this completes the circuit and the lamp lights. To test a heater appliance, one lead of the tester is placed on one prong of the appliance attachment

◆ 75. A continuity tester can be made by connecting a light bulb in series with an attachment plug and test leads.

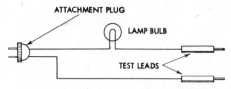

ATTACHMENT PLUG

LAMP BULB

TEST LEADS

◆ 76. This is the wiring diagram of the continuity tester.

plug and the other lead is placed on the other prong, as shown in Photograph 77.

It is important that the two test leads do not touch each other. If the lamp does not light this shows that there is an open circuit and either the element is burned out or that there is a break in the heater cord. If the lamp lights, this would indicate a complete circuit and that the heating unit is good.

Testing for Shorts to the Frame

When one of the electric wires comes in contact with the appliance frame this makes the appliance a dangerous piece of equipment to use. Anyone touching the appliance could easily get an electrical shock. The continuity tester can be used for testing for shorts

to the frame. One lead of the tester is placed on the prongs of the appliance plug and the other lead is touched to the frame of the appliance.

If the lamp lights this shows that there is a complete circuit from the electric wiring to the frame. A complete circuit from the element or from any part of the electric wiring to the frame is often called a *ground*. All grounds must be repaired before the appliance can be used safely.

Checking the Heater Cord

After testing the appliance with the continuity tester and finding either a short or an open circuit, it is then necessary to locate the trouble. Most failures in portable equipment such as flat irons, toasters, waffle irons, and portable heaters occur in the heater cord. The constant bending of these cords breaks the wires. The heater cord should be disconnected from the appliance and the continuity tester used to find out if the cord is at fault. Both wires must be tested to find out if there

◆ 77. An electric iron can be tested with a continuity tester to determine whether the heating unit is good.

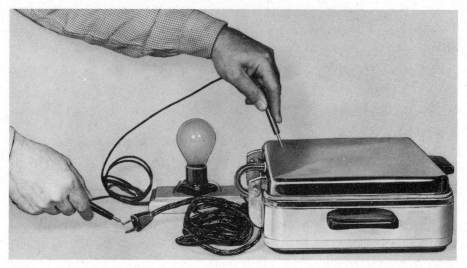

◆ 78. A continuity tester can be used to test a waffle iron for dangerous shorts to the frame.

is continuity or a break in the wires. Also a check must be made to see if the wires are shorted together. If either a short or a break in the cord is located it is probably best to replace the cord with a new one.

Checking the Heater Element

With the cord removed from the appliance, the continuity tester leads can be placed across the two terminals of the heater element as shown in Photograph 80. If the light fails to come on this shows that the element is burned out. In most appliances the burned-out element cannot be rewound but the entire element must be replaced. The old unit, including the heater wire and the insulating material, must be removed and a new unit installed.

◆ 79. A continuity tester is used like this to test the cord of an electric appliance for failure.

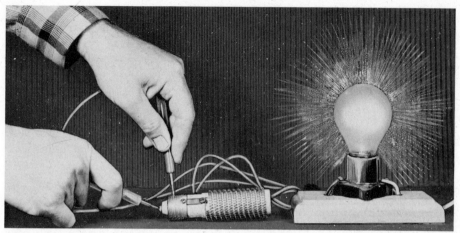

♦ 80. This is how to use a continuity tester to check a heater element for a short or open circuit.

INTERESTING THINGS TO DO

1. Making a Test Lamp.
Materials needed:

1 Wood base, ½" x 3" x 5"
1 Cleat receptacle
1 Attachment plug cap
6′ Lamp cord, parallel, No. 18
2 Insulated test prods
3′ Test lead wire

Secure the cleat receptacle to the wood base with wood screws. Attach the two leads from one end of the lamp cord to the plug cap. Attach one of the leads from the opposite end of the lamp cord to one of the receptacle terminals. Cut the test lead wire into 18" lengths and attach a test prod to one end of each piece. The test prods may be secured from a radio supply house, or made up out of fiber rod and nails. Attach one of the test prod leads to the remaining terminal on the cleat receptacle. Attach the other test prod lead to the remaining lamp cord wire.

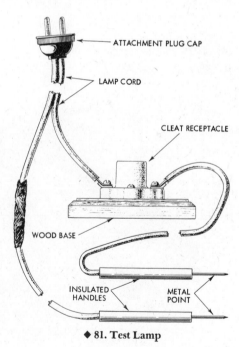

♦ 81. Test Lamp

Solder and tape the connection. See Illustration 81.

2. Constructing an Electric Coffee Warmer.

Materials needed:

1 Coffee can (1-pound size), with lid
1 Piece asbestos transite, circular, 3/16″ thick. (The diameter will be the same as the inside diameter of the particular coffee can that is used.)
40′ Resistance wire, nichrome, No. 29
2 Machine screws, steel or brass, 6–32, 3″ long
2 Pieces pipe, 1/8″ pipe size, 2¾″ long
6′ Heater cord, asbestos covered, No. 18
1 Rubber grommet, 3/8″ inside diameter
4 Pieces sheet steel, 20 gage, 3/8″ x 1¼″
1 Piece brass rod, round, 1/8″ diameter, 20¼″ long
4 Machine screws, roundhead (RH) steel, 6–32, ¼″ long
6 Machine screw nuts, hexagon, steel, 6–32
2 Machine screws, flathead (FH) brass, 6–32, ½″ long
2 Machine screw nuts, hexagon, brass, 6–32
1 Attachment plug cap

Make a number of 5/16″ holes in the lid of the coffee can, as shown in Photographs 82 and 83. Drill and shape

◆ **82. Coffee Warmer**

the four pieces of sheet steel to serve as legs for the warmer, as shown in the section view, Drawing 84. Drill four 5/32″ holes in the bottom of the can near the outside edge and secure the legs in place with the RH machine screws. Cut the circular piece of asbestos transite so that it will fit the inside of the coffee can. Drill holes and saw slots in the asbestos transite as shown in the drawing. Place two brass machine

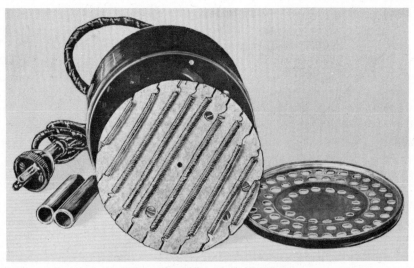

◆ **83. Parts of the Electric Coffee Warmer**

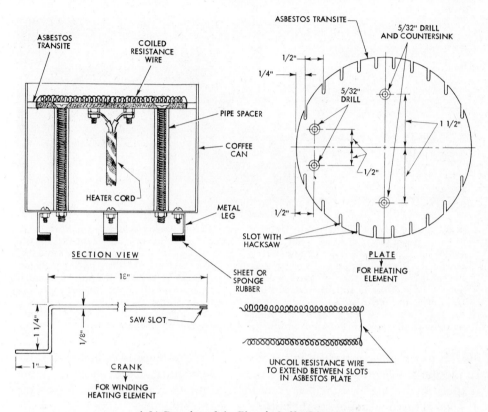

♦ 84. Drawing of the Electric Coffee Warmer

screws in the circular piece to serve as terminal screws.

Bend the piece of round brass rod to the shape as shown in Drawing 84 to serve for winding the heating element. Look at Photograph 85 to see how to wind the element. Remove the coiled wire from the crank carefully and stretch it until it is 32″ long. Secure one end of the coiled wire to one of the terminal screws and place the wire on the circular asbestos piece. When extending the resistance wire from one slot to another, uncoil just enough wire to reach between the slots, as shown on the drawing. Connect the remaining end of the coiled resistance wire to the other terminal screw. Attach one end of the heater cord to the terminal screws. Drill two $\frac{5}{32}$″ holes through the bottom of the coffee can in line with the two holes in the heating unit. Also make a hole in the side of the can near the bottom for the rubber grommet. Place the grommet in the hole and pass the end of the heater cord through it. Secure the completed heating unit to the bottom of the can

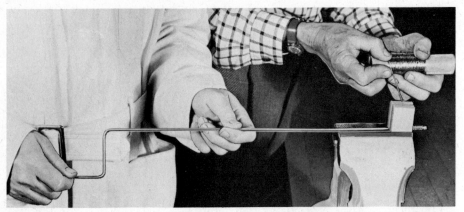

◆ 85. Place the crank illustrated in Drawing 84 between two pieces of wood about 1″ wide and 6″ long, so that about ½″ of rod extends beyond the side of the pieces of wood. Secure the wood pieces in a vise, so that it will require a little effort to turn the crank. Place one end of the nichrome wire in the slot at the end of the brass rod and turn the crank slowly until the turns of resistance wire reach the pieces of wood. Winding the heating element is a job which requires the help of two persons, one to turn the crank and another to feed the resistance wire. Just enough tension should be kept on the wire to wind it tightly on the rod. Once the turns of wire reach the wood pieces, the rod will feed through them automatically until all of the wire is wound on the rod.

with pieces of pipe serving as spacers and the 3″ machine screws. Connect a plug cap to the end of the heater cord. Cement pieces of rubber to the bottom of the legs to prevent marring the table and the project is complete for use.

When plugged into a 115-volt outlet this appliance will produce just the right temperature to keep coffee warm right on the dining table.

REVIEW QUESTIONS

1. Name several types of home appliances that use a heating element.

2. What kind of wire is used in heating elements?

3. Why are calrod heating elements considered a good type of heating element?

4. What is the heat regulator on most electrical appliances called?

5. Explain how a heat regulator used on home appliances operates.

6. Draw a circuit for a continuity tester like the one you learned about.

7. How is a continuity tester used to find out if the heating element is burned out?

8. Explain how a continuity tester is used to determine whether or not there is a ground in a heater appliance.

9. Where do most failures occur in portable heater appliances?

10. Why is it usually necessary to replace most heater elements with new factory-built units?

UNIT 21

THE ELECTRIC MOTOR

Purpose of Electric Motors

The construction of electric motors is very similar to that of electric generators. Just as the generator has a field and an armature so does the electric motor. Generators are used to produce electricity and need to be rotated. The electric motor uses the electricity developed by a generator or a battery to produce motion. Electric motors are used in such devices as fans, refrigerators, sewing machines, vacuum cleaners, washing machines, lathes, circular saws, and motion picture projectors.

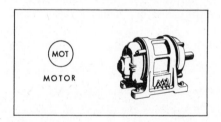

MOTOR

The letters show that the machine is a motor.

Fundamentals of a Simple DC Motor

Motors and generators look very much alike and in some cases generators may be used for motors and some motors can be used for generators. In Units 7 and 15 we learned that a generator produced electricity if a coil was rotated in a magnetic field. The simple generator can be made into a motor to produce motion by connecting a battery to the brushes as in Illustration 86. The armature has a current flowing through the coils and that

makes it an electromagnet. All electromagnets have a north and a south pole so the armature will have a north and a south pole. The permanent field magnet also has a north and a south pole.

The brush on the left-hand side is connected to the positive terminal of the battery and the current flow is such that this side of the armature becomes a north pole. The brush on the right-hand side is connected to the negative terminal of the battery and that side of the armature becomes a south pole. Thus the armature has a north pole next to the north pole of the magnet and a south pole next to the south pole of the magnet. We know that like poles will repel each other and so both poles

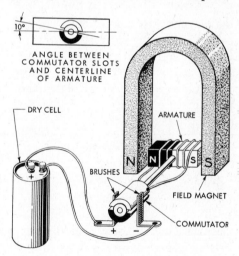

10°

ANGLE BETWEEN COMMUTATOR SLOTS AND CENTERLINE OF ARMATURE

DRY CELL

ARMATURE

N N S S

BRUSHES

FIELD MAGNET

COMMUTATOR

+ −

◆ 86. Armature will start to rotate as poles on the armature repel like poles in the field magnet.

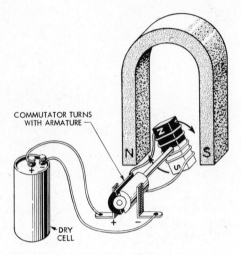

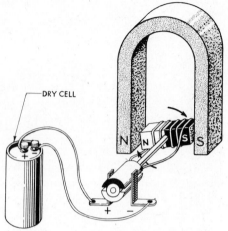

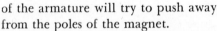

◆ 87. The armature has rotated so that unlike poles now attract each other.

◆ 88. The armature polarity is now changed by the commutator so that again like poles repel each other.

of the armature will try to push away from the poles of the magnet.

This repelling of like poles makes the armature rotate. As the armature rotates, the north pole of the armature is attracted toward the south pole of the magnet. Just before the two poles come together by their attraction for each other the polarity of the armature is changed by the commutator. Again the two like poles repel each other and the armature continues to rotate. See Illustrations 87 and 88.

Motors with Electromagnetic Field Coils

An electromagnet may be used to produce the electromagnetic field instead of a permanent magnet. The electromagnet called a *field coil* consists of insulated wire wound around a steel core. The battery is used to produce the magnetic field for the field coil as well as to provide the current

for the armature. Illustrations 89 and 90 show how the field coils may be connected in series or in parallel with the armature.

Armatures with Several Coils

To improve the operating efficiency of commercial motors several sets of coils may be used in the armature. By using several sets of coils in the armature it is necessary to have a commutator with a number of different segments to connect each of the coils to. In this way the brushes are always in contact with a set of coils that are directly across from the field poles. Using a number of coils in the armature produces a much smoother running motor.

Using Alternating Current on Motors

Some motors may be used on either

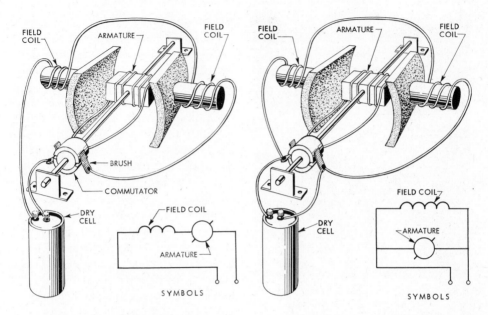

♦ **89. Electric motor with field coil connected in series with the armature coil.**

♦ **90. Electric motor with field coil connected in parallel with armature coil.**

direct current or alternating current. Motors using an electromagnetic field with a commutator may be operated from ac or dc. When alternating current is connected to these motors, the magnetic field is continually changing in both the armature winding and in the field coil winding. Since the currents in both the armature and the field coil are changing together, the polarity of each is changed at the same time. When one pole of the field coil is the north pole the armature pole nearest it is also a north pole and they repel each other. When the direction of current flow changes and this same field pole becomes a south pole, the armature pole is also changed to a south pole and they continue to repel each other. The commutator is the device that makes the rotation of the motor possible.

Universal Motor Repairs

Small motors designed to operate on either alternating or direct current

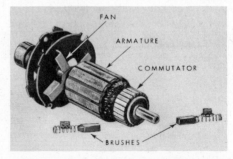

♦ **91. The armature of an electric motor showing the commutator segments. The segments are insulated from each other and are connected to different sets of coils in the armature.**

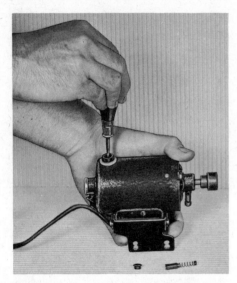

◆ 92. Removing the brushes from an electric motor used on a sewing machine.

are called *universal* motors. These motors have the field coil connected in series with the armature coil as in Illustration 89. This type of small motor is found in vacuum cleaners, fans, sewing machines, electric mixers, and similar household appliances.

The carbon brushes on these universal motors sometimes become worn and must be replaced. When replacing brushes it is important to disconnect the appliance from the electrical circuit before starting to work.

The new brushes should be the same type and size as those used by the manufacturer. The old brushes can be removed by unscrewing the brush-holder screws found on each side of the motor, as shown in Photograph 92. Screws in the end of the brush holders press against a small spring that keeps the brush in contact with the commutator.

The commutator on these motors

◆ 93. Electric motors are made in many sizes and are specially designed to meet particular requirements.

sometimes needs to be cleaned. Usually it is necessary to disassemble the motor to clean the commutator. When taking the motor apart it is advisable to take out the brushes so that they won't become damaged when removing the armature. Use a very fine sandpaper and sand the commutator lightly. When the copper segments on the commutator shine this should be a good indication that the commutator is clean.

Oil should only be used on the bearings of an electric motor. Some motors have cups where the oil is to be placed. Use oil very sparingly and be sure that it does not get on the brushes or the commutator.

Induction Motors

One of the most common types of electric motor used on alternating cur-rent is the *induction* motor. Induction motors are used on refrigerators, garbage disposals, blowers, washing machines, and on many types of machinery. It can only be used on alternating current and does not require a commutator or brushes.

The induction motor consists of two main parts—the *stator,* which is the stationary set of coils wound in the frame of the motor, and the *rotor,* which is the rotating part of the motor. See Photograph 94. The rotor is made of laminated steel with slots cut in it to hold copper bars. The copper bars that are in the slots of the steel core are all connected together at the end by two rings of copper. This type of rotor is called a *squirrel cage* rotor (Photograph 95). The stator acts like a primary of a transformer and induces a current in the rotor.

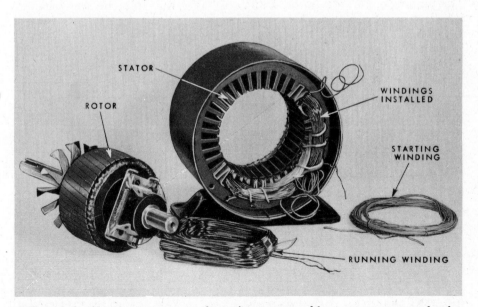

◆ 94. An induction motor operates on alternating current and has no commutator or brushes.

Courtesy General Electric Co.

◆ **95. A squirrel cage rotor as it would appear when removed from the slots of the laminated sheet steel rotor core and reassembled.**

When the magnetic field of the stator induces a current in the copper bars, the rotor becomes an electromagnet. The field of the stator attracts or repels the rotor and pushes it around. This pushing of the rotor by the stator is what makes the motor run. The main advantage of the induction-type motor is that there are no moving parts, such as brushes and commutators, that must be connected in the electrical circuit. Elimination of any direct connection between the stator and the rotor produces a fairly trouble-free motor.

Starting the Induction Motor

Most induction motors require a start to get the rotor moving. The usual method of starting an induction motor is to use two stator windings. One winding is called the *running winding* and the other is called the *starting winding*. See Photograph 96. The starting winding helps to start the rotor moving and is disconnected after the motor has reached running speed. When the starting winding is cut out of the circuit the running winding

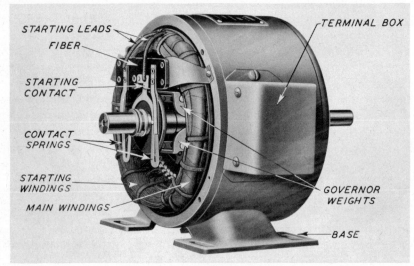

Courtesy General Electric Co.

◆ **96. This is an alternating current motor with one end removed, showing the arrangement of the starting switch.**

keeps the motor going. An automatic cut-out switch is arranged so that as the speed of the motor picks up it will open and disconnect the starting wind-ing from the circuit. When the motor stops, the switch automatically closes and the starting winding is again in the circuit.

INTERESTING THINGS TO DO

1. Tin Can Motor.
Materials needed:

2 Pieces tin, 1/2″ x 5 1/4″ (cut from a tin can)
2 Pieces tin, 1/2″ x 1 7/8″
1 Piece steel rod, 1/16″ x 2 1/2″
2 Pieces sheet brass, 3/8″ x 1 1/4″, 16 gage
2 Pieces spring brass, 1/4″ x 1 1/8″, 26 gage
1 Piece brass tubing, 1/4″ inside diameter,
  1/2″ long, 22 gage
1 Piece fiber rod, round, 1/4″ diameter,
  1/2″ long
1 Piece wood, 1/2″ x 2 1/2″ x 3″
1 Piece wood, 3/8″ x 1/2″ x 3/4″
2 Terminal screws, 6–32, 1″ long
1 Spool magnet wire, No. 24, cotton- or
  enamel-covered

◆ **97. A Tin Can Motor**

Lay out and drill the two pieces of tin as shown in the drawing for the field coil frame. See Drawing 98. Place the two pieces together and solder along the edges near the center. Bend the two pieces to the shape shown and solder the remaining edges together. Wrap the flat end of the completed field coil frame with tape or thin cardboard and wind four layers of magnet wire over the tape or cardboard. Drill a 5/32″ hole through the small wood block and through the wood base and secure the field frame to the wood base with a roundhead machine screw. Shape the smaller pieces of tin as shown in the drawing to serve as the armature frame and solder the two pieces together along the edges. Insert the piece of round steel rod through the center of the armature frame and solder it to the frame. Wrap the arma-ture frame with tape or thin cardboard and, starting at the center near the shaft, wind four layers of magnet wire on each side of the armature. Both coils should be wound in the same di-rection and the winding should begin and end at the center of the frame, so that the ends of the coil may be con-nected directly to the commutator.

Drill a hole through the center of the fiber rod, so that it will fit tightly on the shaft. Cut the brass tubing lengthwise into two equal sections, place the sections on the fiber rod, and secure them by winding a number of turns of thread around one end of the brass tubing. Allow enough space be-tween the thread and the end of the brass tubing, so that the thread will not be burned when the armature wires are soldered in place. This com-pletes the commutator.

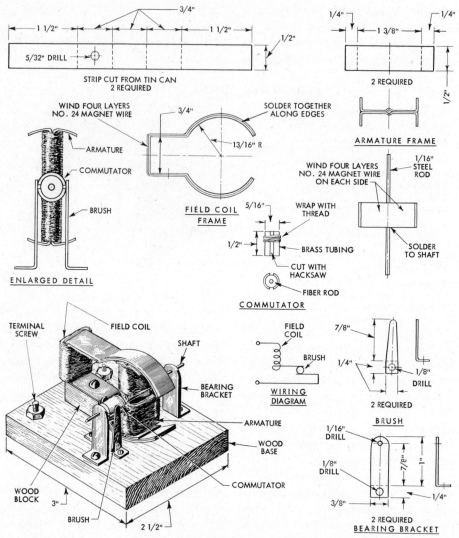

◆ **98. Tin Can Motor Parts and Assembly**

Place the commutator on the steel shaft, next to the armature, so that the slots in the commutator are on each side of the armature. Solder the ends of the armature windings to the section of the commutator that is on the same side of the shaft.

Drill and shape the two pieces of sheet brass to serve as bearing brackets, as shown in the drawing. Place the brackets on the armature shaft and secure the brackets to the wood base with 4–40 machine screws. Drill and shape the two pieces of spring brass to serve as brushes, as shown in the drawing.

Mount the brushes on the wood base, one on each side of the commutator, with 4–40 machine screws. The tension of the brushes should be adjusted so that they make good contact with the commutator, but they should not be so tight that they prevent the armature from turning properly.

When the proper position for the armature and commutator has been found, small machine screw nuts may be soldered to the shaft close to the outside of the bearing brackets, to keep the armature centered.

Make the connections for the motor by running a wire on the bottom of the wood base from a terminal screw to one of the brush screws. Connect one of the field coil wires to the remaining brush screw. Connect the other field coil lead to the remaining terminal. The motor should now be ready for its initial tryout. Although the motor was designed to run on the transformer that was described in another unit, it will run on other sources of power, such as dry cells or a storage battery. Depending upon the speed of rotation desired, any voltage between 4 and 10 volts may be used.

2. Alternating Current Motor.
Materials needed:

1 Piece steel rod, round, ⅜″ diameter, 1″ long
1 Piece band steel, ⅛″ x ¾″ x 11″
2 Pieces steel rod, round, ½″ diameter, ⅝″ long
1 Piece steel rod, round, ⅛″ diameter, 3¾″ long
1 Spool magnet wire, No. 24, enamel- or cotton-covered
4 Washers, fiber, 1/16″ thick, ⅞″ diameter
1 Piece wood, ½″ x 3″ x 6″
2 Machine screws, FH, steel, 10–24, 1″ long
2 Terminal screws

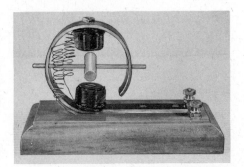

♦ 99. An Alternating Current Motor

This easily made motor will rotate at a speed of 3,600 revolutions a minute on 60-cycle alternating current, but unlike a motor that has a commutator and brushes it is not self-starting. It will run only on low-voltage alternating current and it was designed to work with the transformer that is described in Unit 16 of this book. The motor operates on the principle that the rotor will go around to keep in step with the change of direction of the current that flows through the field coils and, since the current is changing at the rate of 3,600 times a minute, the rotor will also rotate at a similar speed.

Shape the piece of band steel so that one end will form a circle 2½″ in diameter and drill holes in it as indicated on Drawing 100. Locate the holes exactly in the middle across the width of the band steel. Drill ¼″ holes through the center of the pieces of ½″ steel rod. Drill ½″ holes in the center of the fiber washers and place a washer over each end of the pieces of steel rod to make the field coil form. Countersink one of the washers on each form so that the head of the screw which holds it in place will be even with the fiber. See Photograph 99. Wind each

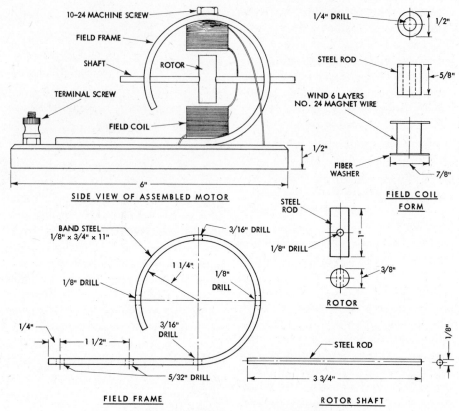

♦ **100. Alternating Current Motor Drawing**

form with six layers of No. 24 magnet wire and secure the completed coil to the field frame with 10–24 machine screws and nuts. Make a temporary connection between one wire from each field coil and connect the remaining two wires to a dry cell. Place your magnetic compass near one of the field coils and note which end of the compass needle is attracted to the coil. Now place your compass near the other field coil and note which end of the compass is attracted to it. If each coil attracts a different pole of the compass they are connected correctly and the connection between them can be made permanent. If both coils attract the same end of the compass, the coil connections will have to be reversed before the permanent connection is made. Secure the field frame to the wood base with wood screws and connect two wires from the field coils to the terminal screws by passing the wires through the base and connecting them to the heads of the screws.

Drill a hole through the middle of the ⅜″ steel rod to serve as the rotor, as shown on the drawing. Place the rotor in the field frame between the two field coils. Insert the rotor shaft through one of the $\frac{1}{8}''$ holes in the frame, the hole in the rotor, and the hole in the opposite side of the frame. Place the rotor at the exact center of the rotor shaft and solder it to the shaft. The motor is now ready to run.

Connect the motor to your trans-former, grasp the rotor shaft between a thumb and forefinger and spin the shaft. The first few attempts at start-ing the motor may not be successful, but once you learn the knack of the proper amount to spin the shaft, start-ing the motor will be easy.

REVIEW QUESTIONS

1. Name several uses for electrical motors.

2. What is the purpose of the com-mutator on a simple motor?

3. Draw a diagram of a simple mo-tor using an electromagnetic field.

4. Why do motor armatures some-times have several sets of coils?

5. Why can some motors be used on both direct current and alternating current? What are the motors called?

6. How are commutators cleaned?

7. Name two important parts of an induction motor.

8. What is one of the main advan-tages of an induction motor?

9. Explain the construction of a squirrel cage rotor.

10. What are the two windings used in an induction motor called?

UNIT 22
THE AUTOMOBILE ELECTRICAL SYSTEM

The modern automobile uses elec-tricity in many ways. Electricity is used to (1) crank the engine, (2) provide lights for night driving, (3) ignite the fuel that gives power to the engine, (4) operate instruments such as fuel

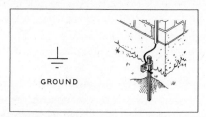

GROUND

This symbol is used for actual ground to earth or to frame or chassis.

gage, temperature gage, and oil pres-sure gage, (5) light signaling devices such as stop lights and turning lights, and (6) operate many accessories such as radios, horns, heaters, and windows. The complete wiring for the automo-bile requires many circuits as shown in Diagram 101.

The Storage Battery

We learned about the storage bat-tery in Unit 6. It is a very good source of electricity because it can deliver large amounts of current and can be recharged when run down. Each cell

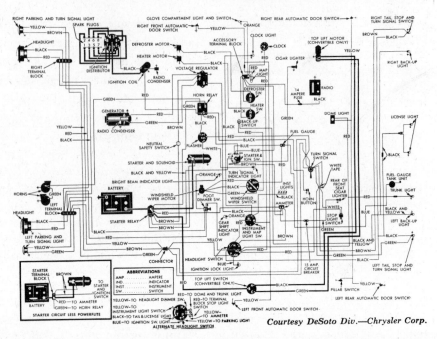

Courtesy DeSoto Div.—Chrysler Corp.

◆ **101. This diagram of a typical wiring system clearly shows how necessary electricity is to the operation of an automobile.**

of a storage battery delivers 2 volts. To obtain 12 volts from a storage battery it is necessary to have six cells connected in series, as shown in Illustration 102. A 6-volt storage battery has three cells connected in series. Automobiles use either 6-volt or 12-volt storage batteries.

To reduce the number of wires used for the electrical circuits in the automobile the steel frame of the chassis is used as one wire in the circuit. This is possible because the low voltage of the battery is not dangerous. Some automobile manufacturers design their engines to have the negative terminal of the battery connected to the frame and others connect the positive terminal to the frame. The battery terminal

connected to the frame is said to be *grounded* to the frame. A heavy flexible cable called a *ground cable* is used for this purpose. See Photograph 103.

The Starting Motor

The automobile uses a direct current motor to crank the engine and get it started. Modern engines are difficult to turn over and the motor called the *starting motor* must be very powerful. The principle of the direct current motor was discussed in Unit 21. Photograph 104 shows the construction of a starting motor.

The battery provides the current necessary to rotate the engine. When the starter switch is pushed down this completes the circuit and the engine

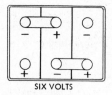

SIX VOLTS

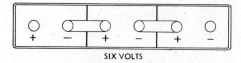

SIX VOLTS

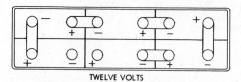

TWELVE VOLTS

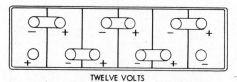

TWELVE VOLTS

From Automotive Electrical Systems,
American Technical Society

◆ 102. **Typical cell arrangements for 6-volt and 12-volt automobile storage batteries are shown here.**

starts. The starting motor shaft is coupled to the engine flywheel and as it rotates it turns the engine over.

In cranking the engine the starting motor draws a large amount of current from the storage battery. The amount of current varies from 150 to 500 amperes, depending upon the design of the motor.

The Generator

The storage battery can supply the electrical needs of the automobile for only a short time. A generator is needed to charge the battery and to help provide current for the rest of the electrical system. The generator is usually driven by a belt that is coupled to the engine.

The direct current generator was discussed in Unit 7. To generate electricity an armature coil is rotated in a magnetic field. The brushes collect the direct current from the commutator and this current is used throughout the automobile.

After the engine has been started by the starting motor, the generator is rotated by the engine and it begins generating direct current. As the generator builds up voltage it charges the battery. This is indicated on the ammeter found on the dashboard of the automobile. The ammeter needle moves to the right when the generator is charging and moves to the left when it is not charging. In some automobiles a warning red light on the dashboard indicates that the generator is not

Courtesy Nash Motors Div.—Nash-Kelvinator Corp.

◆ 103. **This is how a battery is properly mounted in a vehicle.**

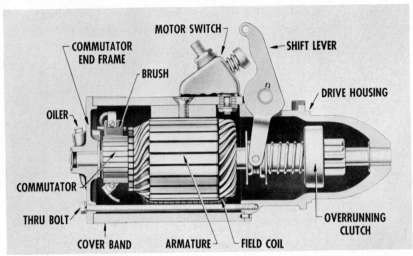

Courtesy Delco-Remy Div.—General Motors Corp.

◆ 104. This illustration shows the construction of a direct current motor used to start an automobile.

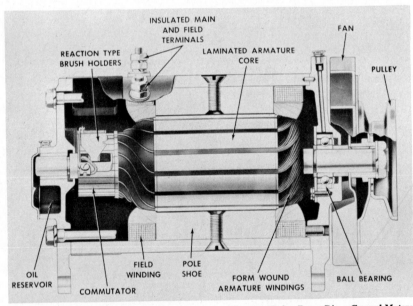

Courtesy Delco-Remy Div.—General Motors Corp.

◆ 105. The construction of a two-brush automobile generator is shown in this illustration.

charging. When the generator is charging the light goes out.

A special device called a *generator regulator* (Photograph 106) is used to keep the voltage supplied by the generator from going too high. The generator regulator, often called the *voltage regulator,* provides an automatic control on the voltage output of the generator. The voltage regulator usually prevents the voltage from the generator from going higher than 7.2 to 7.4 volts in a 6-volt system. On a 12-volt system the voltage is regulated from 14.0 to 14.2 volts. A voltage slightly higher than the battery voltage is needed for the generator to charge the battery. Through the use of this generator regulator the voltage of the entire electrical system remains fairly constant. See Illustration 107.

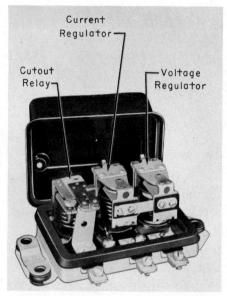

Courtesy Delco-Remy Div.—General Motors Corp.

◆ **106. Generator regulators control the voltage supplied by an automobile generator.**

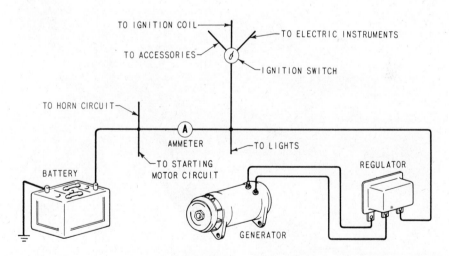

From Automotive Fuel and Ignition Systems, American Technical Society

◆ **107. This basic wiring circuit for an automobile shows the generator and the regulator, which maintains constant voltage.**

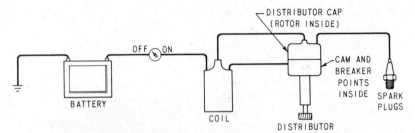

From Automotive Fuel and Ignition Systems, *American Technical Society*

♦ 108. These are the basic parts of an automobile battery-and-coil ignition system that ignites the fuel.

The Ignition System

The ignition system of the automobile is used to ignite the gasoline that powers the engine. The system used in most automobiles is called the battery-and-coil ignition system. See Illustration 108. The spark plugs are placed in the engine so that they can ignite the gas fuel in each of the cylinders. A very high voltage is needed to jump across the gap that is found at the bottom of the plug (Photograph 109). This high voltage is developed through the use of a transformer called an *ignition coil* (Illustration 110). The ignition coil has a primary winding with about 200 to 300 turns of heavy wire

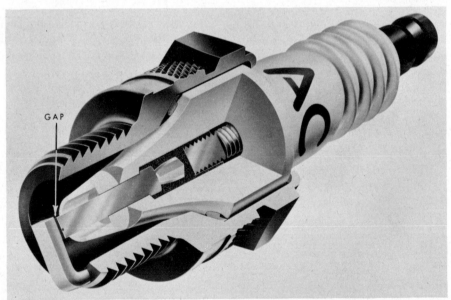

Courtesy General Motors Corp.

♦ 109. Construction of a spark plug. The spark from the ignition coil jumps across the gap to ignite the fuel.

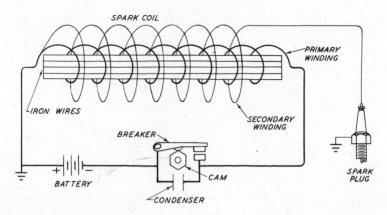

◆ 110. To open and close the breaker points a cam is rotated by the engine. The breaker points are connected in the primary circuit of the ignition coil. As the cam rotates, the breaker points open and close and this starts and stops the current flowing in the primary winding. As the current in the primary starts and stops, a current is induced in the secondary of the ignition coil. Since the secondary has a large number of turns of wire the voltage is stepped up, and when it goes to the spark plug the voltage jumps across the gap in the plug. This spark ignites the engine fuel.

wrapped around a steel core. The secondary coil consists of 16,000 to 23,000 turns of fine magnet wire wrapped on the same steel core as the primary winding. This type of transformer is able to step up the secondary voltage to as high as 20,000 volts.

Since both the battery and the generator produce direct current it is necessary to start and stop the current in the primary winding in order to induce a current in the secondary winding. This is done through the use of breaker points and a cam located in the *distributor* of the engine. A device called a *condenser* is placed across the breaker points to help increase the amount of spark produced by the ignition coil. (In electronics work, the term *condenser* has been replaced by *capacitor*.)

Inside of the distributor is a rotor that turns with the cam. This rotor is connected to the high-voltage secondary of the ignition coil. Coming out the top of the distributor cap is a set of ignition wires. These wires connect to each of the spark plugs. When the engine is running the rotor turns so that it is making contact with each of the spark plug wires one at a time. This permits the high voltage developed by the secondary of the ignition coil to go to each of the spark plugs.

Automobile Lights

Good lights are very important requirements for the safe use of an automobile. The laws of most states require that the headlights must provide enough light to enable one to see objects at least 350' ahead. In addition tail lights, stop lights, and license plate lights are all required by law.

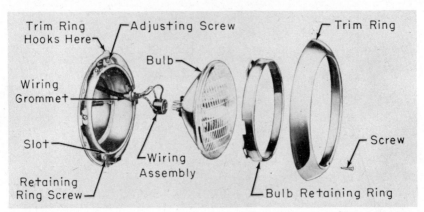

Courtesy Ford Motor Co.

◆ 111. Sealed-beam headlights are constructed so as to keep out dirt, moisture and corrosion.

Headlights are of the sealed-beam type (Photograph 111). Since the entire unit is sealed against dirt, moisture, and corrosion, there is little loss in the amount of light produced by the

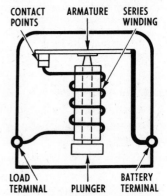

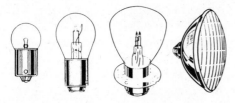

Courtesy General Electric Co.

◆ 112. Illustrated here are types of bulbs used in automobile headlights.

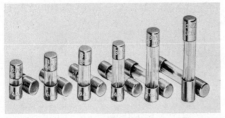

Courtesy Littelfuse Inc.

◆ 113. These are typical fuses used in automotive vehicles.

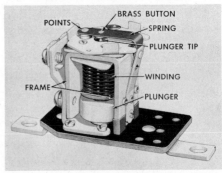

From Automotive Fuel and Ignition Systems, *American Technical Society*

◆ 114. A circuit breaker used in automobiles. If too much current flows through the coil the plunger forces the armature upward and opens the contact points.

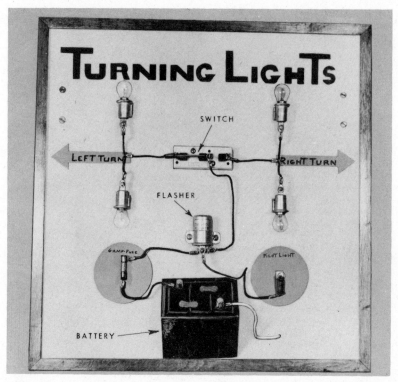

♦ 115. The circuit of a directional turn indicator. Note that only one pilot light is shown. In a two pilot light system the switching would be much more complicated.

sealed beam throughout its life. These sealed units include the bulb, which consists of two filaments, the glass lens, and the reflector.

The bulbs are an incandescent type that will operate off the low voltage produced by the battery or the generator. The sealed-beam headlight has two filaments. One filament produces the light for the upper beam used in country driving. The other filament produces the passing beam light, which is focused downward. A switch called a *dimmer switch* mounted on the left side of the floor board is used to select either the upper or lower beam. When the upper headlight beam is turned on, a beam indicator bulb on the dashboard lights up, producing a small spot of red light. On some automobiles this lowering and raising of the beam is done automatically by means of a photoelectric cell. This photoelectric cell is operated by the light from an approaching automobile.

Protecting Automobile Circuits

Fuses or circuit breakers (Illustrations 113 and 114) are used to protect the lighting and accessory circuits in the automobile. These protective devices are used to prevent the wires from

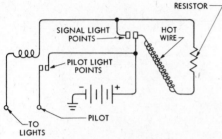

From Automotive Fuel and Ignition Systems,
American Technical Society

◆ **116. The basic circuit of the flasher switch used on directional signal lights. When the switch is turned on, current flows through the "hot wire" and resistor. The resistor in the circuit prevents the bulb from lighting. The "hot wire" has current flowing through it, making it expand. As it expands, the signal light points come together and the bulb lights, because the resistor is shorted out of the circuit. The coil near the pilot light points has enough current flowing through it to pull the points closed and light the arrow on the dashboard. As soon as the current stops flowing through the hot wire it cools, contracts and opens the signal light points. The bulb is turned off but as the "hot wire" heats again the points are closed and again the bulb lights. This heating and cooling of the "hot wire" is what makes the bulb flash off and on.**

becoming damaged if a short circuit occurs. If either a fuse "blows out" or the circuit breakers open the circuit, it is important to locate the trouble and repair it before turning the switch on again.

Directional Signal Lights

Directional signal lights that indicate whether the driver is going to turn right or left have become a very useful accessory on automobiles. The lights mounted on the front and rear of the automobile flash on and off at the rate of almost 90 times per minute. When the switch lever mounted on the steering column is turned on, an indicator bulb on the dashboard also flashes. This indicator bulb shows a small arrow of light to indicate to the driver the direction which the outside lights are flashing. See Illustrations 115 and 116.

INTERESTING THINGS TO DO

Ignition and Spark Plug Tester.
Materials needed:

1 Piece fiber tubing, ½" outside diameter, 1⁄16" wall, 7" long
2 Pieces wood dowel, ⅜" diameter, ½" long
1 Radio resistor, 4.7 megohms, ½-watt
1 Neon lamp, 1⁄25-watt, type NE–2
3' Stranded radio hook-up wire
1 Battery clip
1 Box nail, 6-penny

This handy tester will help locate trouble in your automobile ignition system. When the clip is attached to some metal part of the frame or engine and the pointed end of the tester is placed in contact with the top of the

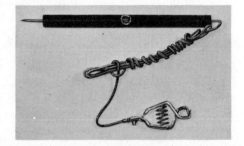

◆ **117. Ignition and Spark Plug Tester**

spark plug, the neon lamp will light up brilliantly, if the spark plug and distributor are operating properly. If the neon lamp lights up dimly or fails

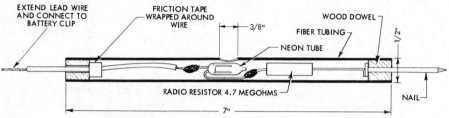

EXTEND LEAD WIRE
AND CONNECT TO
BATTERY CLIP

FRICTION TAPE
WRAPPED AROUND
WIRE

3/8"

WOOD DOWEL

FIBER TUBING

1/2"

NEON TUBE

RADIO RESISTOR 4.7 MEGOHMS

NAIL

7"

◆ **118. Drawing of Ignition and Spark Plug Tester**

to light at all, either the spark plug or distributor is at fault. With a defective distributor the neon lamp will show reduced light on all of the spark plugs. When little or no light shows at only one or two spark plugs, the trouble can usually be traced to defective plugs.

File a section of the fiber tubing at the center with a rat-tail file, so that the electrodes of the neon lamp will be visible. Drill a hole through one of the sections of wood dowel slightly smaller than the box nail and press the nail through the hole. Solder one end of the radio resistor to the head of the nail. Connect the other end of the resistor to one of the neon lamp leads. The resistor and neon lamp should be spaced and connected, so that the neon

lamp will be at the center hole in the fiber tubing when they are inserted into the tubing, as shown in the drawing. Connect the piece of radio hook-up wire to the remaining lead on the neon lamp and wrap the wire with a strip of friction tape close to where it will pass through the section of wood dowel. This will prevent any strain on the neon lamp leads. Insert the assembled neon lamp and resistor into the tubing and glue the wood dowel with the nail in place. Drill a ⅛" hole through the remaining piece of wood dowel, pass the hook-up wire through it, and glue it in the end of the fiber tubing. Attach a battery clip to the end of the hook-up wire and the tester is ready to use.

REVIEW QUESTIONS

1. Name several uses for electricity in the automobile.

2. How many cells are used in a 12-volt storage battery?

3. How is the chassis of the automobile used as part of the electrical circuit?

4. Why does the storage battery need to be in excellent condition to start an engine?

5. What is the purpose of a generator in an automobile?

6. Why is a voltage regulator necessary?

7. Explain the purpose of an ignition coil.

8. How is the distributor used in the automobile ignition circuit?

9. What is the purpose of the spark plugs?

10. Why are sealed-beam lights used?

11. What methods are used to protect automobile electrical circuits?

Using

Electricity

for Communication

〜〜〜〜〜〜〜〜〜〜〜〜〜〜〜〜〜〜〜〜〜〜〜〜〜〜〜〜〜〜

UNIT 23

THE TELEPHONE

The modern telephone is one of the most frequently used electrical devices. It can change sound into a flow of electric current that can be sent over long distances and then change the current back into sound. The telephone was invented by Alexander Graham Bell, who sent the first message over a telephone circuit on March 10, 1876.

Sound Waves

Sound is made by a movement of air. This movement of air is called *air vibrations*. When someone speaks, air is set into waves of vibrations. See Illustration 1. These vibrations hit a human eardrum and sound is heard. Each sound has a different number of

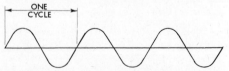

◆ 1. When someone speaks air is set into vibrations. These vibrations are called *sound waves.*

◆ 2. This is the kind of picture used to show a waveform.

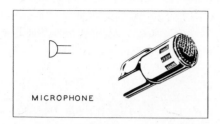

The microphone symbol is simple to draw.

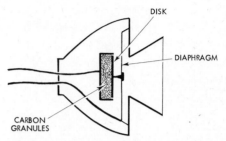

♦ 3. Construction of a telephone microphone.

vibrations per second. The number of vibrations per second is called the *frequency*.

Vibrating frequencies that can be heard by the human ear range from 20 cycles per second to about 20,000 cycles per second. They are called *audio frequencies* because they are audible to the human ear. A frequency of 15,000 cycles per second is a very high-pitched vibration that very few people can hear. Vibrating frequencies are often drawn in picture form as shown in Illustration 2.

The Telephone Transmitter

The part of the telephone into which you speak is the telephone transmitter, called a *microphone*. A simple microphone consists of a round, thin,

flexible diaphragm connected to a small cup that holds some grains of carbon. See Illustration 3. These grains of carbon are called *carbon granules;* they are made of roasted coal. The granules are held in the cup of a round disk that can move back and forth in the cup. This disk is connected to the diaphragm by a small rod. When voice waves hit the diaphragm it moves with the sound vibrations. The vibration of the diaphragm makes the small disk move inside of the cup of carbon. As the diaphragm is moved back and forth the carbon grains are packed more closely and then less closely.

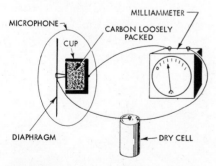

♦ 4. Carbon granules of a microphone are loosely packed and provide a resistance to the current flow. The milliammeter shows that some current is flowing in the circuit.

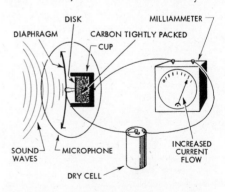

♦ 5. Sound wave pushes diaphragm back and packs carbon granules together; when granules are closer together the resistance of the cup of granules is lowered. Current flow, as shown by the milliammeter, is increased as resistance is reduced.

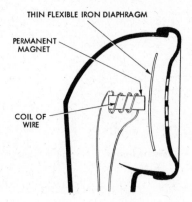

THIN FLEXIBLE IRON DIAPHRAGM

PERMANENT MAGNET

COIL OF WIRE

◆ 6. A telephone receiver construction is shown here.

If a battery is connected across the cup as shown in Illustration 4, a current would flow through the carbon, since it is a conductor of electricity. The carbon acts like a resistor connected across the battery. When the diaphragm moves as in Illustration 5, the carbon is packed closer together and more current will flow through the circuit. The current increases because as the carbon granules move closer together the resistance of the circuit is reduced. We know that more resistance reduces the flow of electricity and less resistance increases the flow of electricity. When the diaphragm moves

back the carbon grains become loosely packed and the current is reduced because the resistance in the circuit is increased.

The current flowing through the circuit will vary with the vibrations of the air waves that hit the diaphragm. The microphone produces a changing electric current that is varied with the sound waves.

The Telephone Receiver

The part of the telephone that is held to the ear is called a *receiver*. The telephone receiver must be able to change the electric current produced by the microphone back into sound waves. A simple receiver consists of a permanent magnet with a coil of wire wound around it and a thin flexible iron diaphragm mounted in front of the magnet and coil. See Illustration 6. The permanent magnet attracts the iron diaphragm and pulls it in slightly. When a current flows through the coil it becomes an electromagnet. The diaphragm has two magnets working on it —the permanent magnet and the electromagnet. If the current through the coil is changing, it will either increase

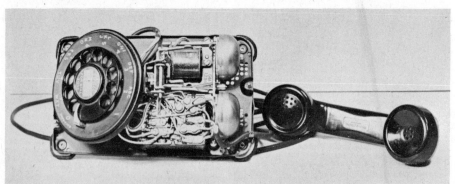

◆ 7. The illustration shows how interior parts of a modern dial telephone are arranged.

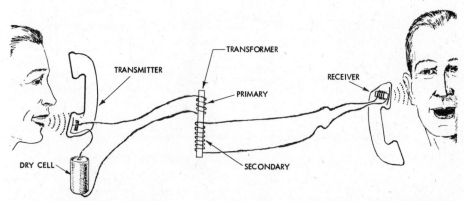

◆ 8. A simple telephone circuit using a step-up transformer to couple the transmitter to the receiver.

the pull on the diaphragm or reduce the pull on the diaphragm. The current in the electromagnet moves the diaphragm back and forth. This movement of the diaphragm pushes the air back and forth in front of it. The movement of air in front of the diaphragm produces sound that can be heard by the human ear.

A Simple Telephone Circuit

To connect a telephone transmitter to a telephone receiver it is usually necessary to use a step-up transformer.

The step-up transformer is used to step up the small voltage produced by the microphone so that a much greater voltage is available for the receiver. See Illustration 8. The primary of the transformer is connected to the microphone and the secondary is connected to the receiver. The varying direct current produced by the movement of the carbon granules in the microphone induces an alternating current in the secondary of the transformer. The stepped-up secondary voltage is used to move the diaphragm of the receiver.

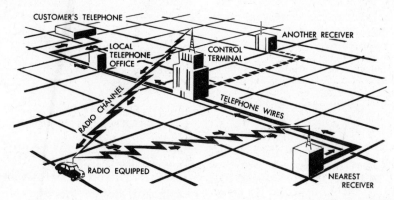

Courtesy Bell Systems

◆ 9. The mobile radiotelephone service in cities makes it possible to place and receive telephone calls in an automobile.

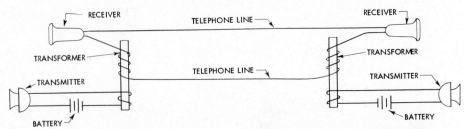

◆ 10. This is how the connections for a two-way telephone circuit are made.

A Two-Way Telephone Circuit

To have a two-way telephone circuit it is necessary to have a receiver and a transmitter at each end of the line, as shown in Illustration 10. A step-up transformer is also used at each location. The two lines connecting the telephones together may be some distance apart. When the phones must be located several miles apart the resistance of the wire lines reduces the strength of the current so that the receiver diaphragm will not move. To increase the strength of such telephone circuits an amplifier is needed. If the telephones are many miles apart a number of different amplifiers located along the route must be used.

INTERESTING THINGS TO DO

Making a Carbon Microphone.
Materials required:

1 Piece wood, 1/2" x 2" x 3"
1 Piece sheet steel or brass, 1/2" x 9 1/2", 24 gage
1 Metal bottle cap, approximately 1 1/4" diameter
1 Felt washer, outside diameter to fit inside of bottle cap
1 Piece sheet brass, circular, diameter 1/8" less than inside of bottle cap
1 Piece thin cardboard, circular, 3 1/8" diameter
2 Machine screws, FH, brass, 6–32, 3/4" long
5 Machine screw nuts, hexagon, brass, 6–32
1 Machine screw, RH, brass, 4–40, 1/4" long
2 Machine screw nuts, hexagon, brass, 4–40
1 Machine screw, RH, steel, 6–32, 1/2" long
1 Piece carbon rod (removed from an old dry cell)

Drill the strip of sheet metal as shown in Drawing 12 and bend it to form a ring 3" in diameter. Solder the

◆ 11. The Carbon Microphone

two ends together where they overlap. Drill 1/8" holes through the center of the brass disk and the circular piece of cardboard. Secure the brass disk to

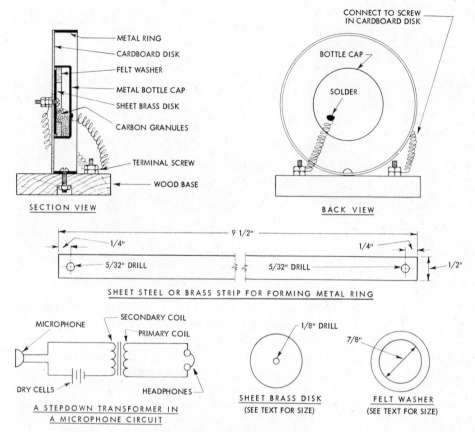

♦ 12. Drawing of the Carbon Microphone

the cardboard with the 4–40 machine screw and hexagon nut. Glue the felt washer to the brass disk so that the head of the brass machine screw is exactly in the center of the washer.

Crush the carbon rod into small pieces about $\frac{1}{16}''$ in diameter. For best results the broken pieces of carbon should be screened through a piece of window screen. Fill the bottle cap about three-fourths full with the carbon granules. Cement the cardboard circle to the bottle cap, making cer-

tain that the felt washer fits snugly inside the bottle cap. Cement the cardboard circle containing the bottle cap to the metal ring. Trim the cardboard to the same size as the metal ring after the cement has set.

Drill a $\frac{5}{32}''$ hole through the center of the wood base and secure the metal ring to it with a 6–32 machine screw. Drill two $\frac{5}{32}''$ holes in the wood base and place flathead machine screws in them to serve as terminals. Solder a piece of No. 30 magnet wire to the

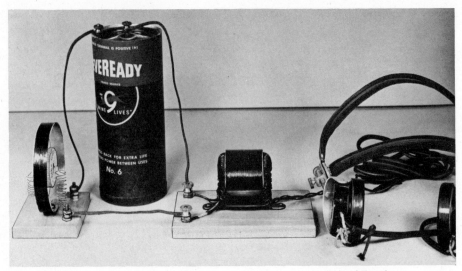

◆ 13. The Microphone Connected to a Transformer and a Pair of Earphones

back of the bottle cap and connect the opposite end to one of the terminal screws. Connect another piece of No. 30 wire to the screw in the center of the cardboard and connect the opposite end to the remaining terminal screw. The microphone is now ready to operate.

A simple circuit for a microphone may be made by connecting the microphone in series with two dry cells and a pair of headphones. A much improved circuit, shown in Photograph 13, may be made by using the transformer which is described in Unit 16. This circuit makes the transformer step up the varying voltages caused by the microphone, so the sound in the headphones is increased many times. With two microphones and two sets of headphones a complete telephone system may be connected together.

REVIEW QUESTIONS

1. Who invented the telephone?

2. How is sound made?

3. What are audio frequencies?

4. Name the principal parts of a telephone transmitter.

5. Explain how the carbon granules in a microphone produce a varying electric current.

6. Name the principal parts of a modern handset telephone receiver.

7. Explain how the diaphragm of a telephone receiver produces sound.

8. Draw a simple telephone circuit showing the receiver and transmitter.

9. Why is the transformer used?

10. When two telephones are a long distance apart, what must be used to increase the signal strength?

UNIT 24
RECEIVING RADIO WAVES

Radio Frequencies

A radio receiver is a standard article in almost every home. In addition to its use in the home, it is also used to provide communication between ships at sea, to control airplanes, to guide air missiles, and for many other purposes. Radio signals cannot be seen but are being sent out in every direction by many types of radio stations. These radio signals are called *radio waves*.

Radio waves are produced by alternating current that is changing directions of flow very rapidly. We learned that audio frequencies range from 20 cycles per second to 20,000 cycles per second. These are the frequencies that are used to produce sound. Radio waves are made up of alternating current that has a frequency that is greater than 20,000 cycles per second. There are a great many radio waves; some have a frequency as high as 300 million cycles per second or more. Radio broadcasting stations that are received by a standard broadcast receiver have frequencies from 535,000 cycles per second to 1,605,000 cycles per second.

Because radio frequencies have such a large number of cycles per second it is usual to express the frequency in *kilocycles* per second. *Kilo* means one thousand. A broadcast station that states that it is operating on a frequency of 600 kilocycles means that its frequency is 600,000 cycles per second.

Courtesy National Broadcasting Co.

◆ 14. These are the transmitting towers of the NBC 50,000-watt station WRCA, Port Washington, Long Island.

ANTENNA

This symbol may be used for any antenna.

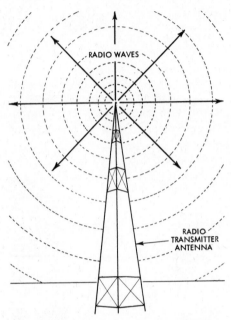

♦ 15. Radio waves leave the transmitting antenna going out in every direction.

Sending Out Radio Waves

When very rapid alternating currents, called *radio frequencies,* flow through a wire they tend to leave the wire and to start traveling through space. They go out in every direction.

At a broadcast station a large transmitter is used to generate radio-frequency waves. The transmitter is connected to a tower called an *antenna.* The radio waves flow up the antenna and leave it to go out into the air. See Illustration 15.

Some waves follow the ground and are called *ground waves.* The ground waves do not go very far and soon become too weak to be received. Some radio waves go up into the sky; they are called *sky waves.* The sky waves may go straight out into space and

become lost. Other waves hit a layer of electrified particles called the *Heaviside layer.* The Heaviside layer acts like a mirror reflecting the waves back to the earth. See Illustration 16. It is because of the Heaviside layer that radio signals can be received many thousands of miles away from the transmitter. The Heaviside layer varies in height above the earth from 50 to 200 miles.

Radio waves travel at the speed of light, 186,000 miles per second. At this speed, signals are received almost instantly after being sent out.

Putting the Sound with the Radio Waves

When we tune a radio receiver to a broadcast station we hear the sound of the announcer or music. The sound could not be heard very far if the radio waves were not used to carry it through the air.

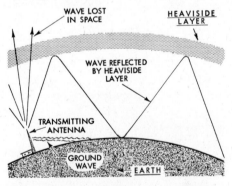

♦ 16. Radio waves go out from the transmitter in all directions. Ground waves follow the ground. Some sky waves are lost in space. Other sky waves hit the Heaviside layer and are reflected back to earth. Waves may be reflected back and forth between the Heaviside layer and the earth so that they sometimes travel very long distances.

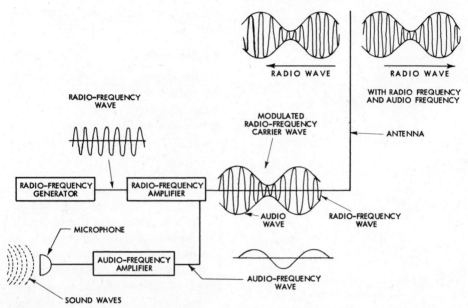

RADIO WAVE

RADIO WAVE

WITH RADIO FREQUENCY
AND AUDIO FREQUENCY

RADIO-FREQUENCY
WAVE

MODULATED
RADIO-FREQUENCY
CARRIER WAVE

ANTENNA

RADIO-FREQUENCY
GENERATOR

RADIO-FREQUENCY
AMPLIFIER

AUDIO
WAVE

RADIO-FREQUENCY
WAVE

MICROPHONE

AUDIO-FREQUENCY
AMPLIFIER

AUDIO-FREQUENCY
WAVE

SOUND WAVES

◆ 17. This block diagram of a transmitter shows how the audio frequencies are combined with the radio-frequency carrier wave.

A microphone similar to the telephone microphone is used in the broadcast station to pick up the sound of the announcer's voice or the music. This voice or music is the audio frequency that we hear when we turn on a radio receiver.

The microphone changes the sound vibrations into a varying electric current. An amplifier is then used to increase the strength of the sound frequencies. After the amplifier makes the audio waves stronger they are combined with the radio waves by the transmitter. The radio-frequency wave being produced by the transmitter is called a *carrier wave* because it carries the audio frequencies with it. Diagram 17 shows what happens when the sound waves are combined with the radio waves. When the audio-fre-

quency waves combine with the radio-frequency wave, at the transmitter, the radio-frequency wave is said to be *modulated.* The purpose of a radio receiver is to tune in on the radio waves and then separate the sound so that it can be heard through the loudspeaker.

Receiving Radio Waves

To receive radio waves it is necessary to have a radio receiver that will tune in the desired stations. Radio receivers use either an outside antenna wire or a wire inside of the cabinet for the antenna. If the receiver is a long distance from the transmitter, an outside wire antenna that has been raised above the housetops will help bring in the waves.

When the radio waves hit the receiver antenna a very weak current will

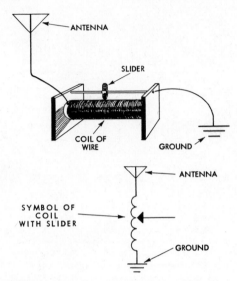

♦ 18. A coil with a slider may be used to tune a radio receiver.

begin to flow in the antenna wire. Since there are a great many stations all sending out radio signals, a number of different radio-frequency currents can be coming in contact with the receiving antenna at the same time. It then becomes necessary to be able to select only one station at a time. A *tuner* is used in the receiver to tune in each of the different stations. When we turn the dial of a radio receiver, we are adjusting the tuner to the station that we wish to hear.

The Ground System

The tuner of a radio receiver is connected to the antenna and also to the ground. The ground may be a wire connected to a water pipe or sometimes to the metal frame of the radio receiver. Every electrical circuit requires two paths for the current to flow through. In a radio signal the air is one path, and the ground is the other path.

Tuning with a Coil

The purpose of the tuner is to select the station that is sending out radio waves on a fixed frequency. The tuner must select one frequency and not permit any of the other signals to be heard in the receiver.

One method of making a tuner is to use a coil of wire with a slider that comes in contact with each of the turns on the coil, as shown in Illustration 18. One end of the coil is connected to the antenna, and the ground is connected to the slider. By moving the slider, the length of the coil of wire between the antenna and ground can be changed. When the radio waves strike the antenna a current starts to flow down the antenna and through the coil to ground. The alternating current of the radio waves will flow first in one direction and then in the other direction, as shown in Illustrations 19 and 20. This current is a flow of electrons in the coil, and the more turns of wire used on the coil the longer it will take the electrons to flow through the coil.

When the slider is moved so that only a few turns of wire are connected between the antenna and ground, the electrons can flow through the coil in one direction and then back in the other direction in a very short time.

After the electrons flow through the coil and back again another radio wave strikes the antenna. If this radio wave is in step with the current flowing in the coil, the second wave will start more electrons flowing at the same

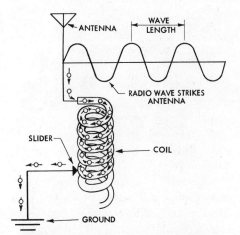

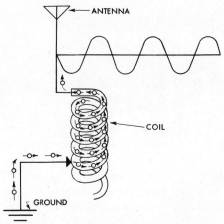

◆ 19. Radio waves hit the antenna and start electrons flowing through coil to ground.

◆ 20. When the alternating current of the radio waves changes direction the electrons flow from ground to antenna.

time that the electrons in the coil are ready to start back again. The coil of wires is then in tune with the radio wave.

The other radio waves that strike the antenna will not be in step with the electron flow in the coil, and they will not be able to flow in the coil. These unwanted radio signals are not accepted by the tuner.

A large number of turns of wire will tune to a low frequency because it takes longer for the electrons to flow through the coil. A small number of turns of wire tune to a high frequency. See Illustrations 21 and 22. When the coil is tuned to a particular frequency it is said to be in *resonance* with that frequency.

Tuning with a Variable Capacitor

Another method of tuning a radio

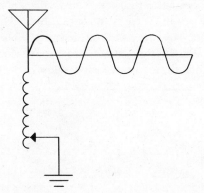

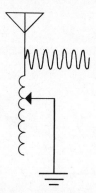

◆ 21. The tuner receives low-frequency stations when there are many turns of wire in the coil between the antenna and ground.

◆ 22. The tuner receives higher frequency stations when there are very few turns between the antenna and ground.

◆ 23. Three kinds of variable capacitors are shown here. They were formerly called condensers.

receiver is to use a coil of wire with a *variable capacitor* connected across each end of the coil. (*Capacitors* were formerly called *condensers* and the

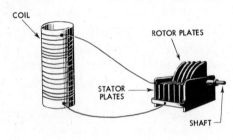

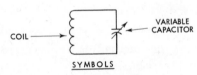

◆ 24. Coil and variable capacitor that are used as a radio tuner.

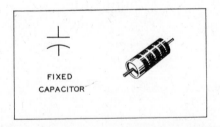

The curved line indicates the outside electrode in fixed paper or ceramic capacitors and the negative electrode of an electrolytic capacitor.

term is still sometimes used.) A variable capacitor consists of a group of metal plates all joined together, called the *stator* plates, and another group of plates all joined together by a shaft so that they can be rotated, called the *rotor* plates. See Illustration 23. The rotor plates slide inside the stator plates without touching each other. Air separates the rotor plates from the stator plates. The variable capacitor has the same effect in tuning the circuit as changing the number of turns on a coil. See Illustrations 24, 25, and 26.

The capacitor acts like a storage place for electrons. It can store either a few electrons or many electrons. When the rotor is turned so that all of the plates are inside of the stator plates the capacitor is able to store more electrons than when it is opened.

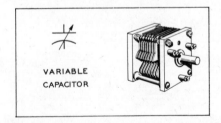

The curved line represents the moving element of a variable capacitor.

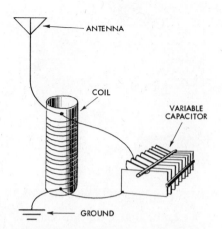

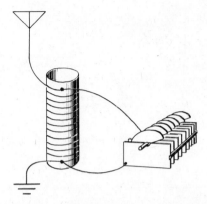

◆ 25. When the variable capacitor is almost closed it stores lots of electrons and tunes to a low frequency. The frequency is determined by the time it takes for all of the electrons to flow from one side of the capacitor through the coil to the other side of the capacitor and then back again.

When the capacitor is closed and stores lots of electrons, the circuit acts like a coil with many turns of wire. It then tunes to a low frequency. See Illustration 27. If the capacitor is opened and the plates are separated, very few electrons are stored. The tuner will now receive higher frequency signals because there will not be as many electrons to flow through the circuit. Each movement of the capacitor tunes the coil to a new frequency.

◆ 26. When the capacitor is opened it stores few electrons. This circuit tunes to a higher frequency.

Capacitance of Variable Capacitors

Variable capacitors are rated by their *capacitance*. The capacitance of variable capacitors is measured in *microfarads* (abbreviated as μf) or *micromicrofarads* (abbreviated as $\mu\mu f$). *Micro* means one millionth. A variable capacitor used to tune broad-

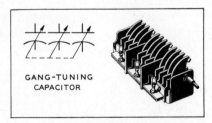

GANG-TUNING CAPACITOR

A dash line is used to indicate that there is a mechanical connection.

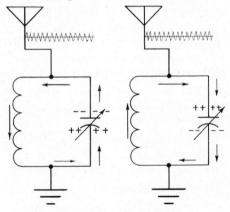

◆ 27. Electrons flow back and forth from one side of the capacitor through the coil to the other side of the capacitor. The frequency of the circuit is determined by the capacitance of the capacitor and the number of turns on the coil.

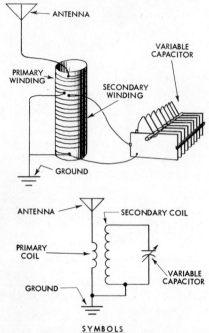

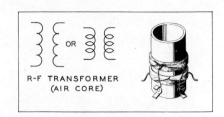

R-F TRANSFORMER
(AIR CORE)

Inductance symbols are arranged this way for a transformer.

SYMBOLS

◆ **28. A radio-frequency transformer is used in a radio tuner.**

Radio-Frequency Transformers

We know that a transformer can be used to step up the voltage. Most radio tuners use a step-up transformer to increase the signal strength. A radio-frequency transformer has a primary and a secondary just like all other transformers.

In the radio tuner the primary of the transformer is connected to the antenna and ground. The secondary is tuned by the variable capacitor, as shown in Illustration 28. The incoming radio waves flow through the primary and induce a current in the secondary. The secondary has more turns than the primary, so the transformer is a step-up transformer. Most radio-frequency transformers do not use an iron core because at high frequencies air becomes a good conductor for the magnetic field. In some radio receivers, instead of a variable capacitor, an iron rod moved inside of the coil is used to tune the receiver.

cast receivers is usually a .00035 micro-farad. This same capacitor in micro-microfarads would be a 350 micromi-crofarad capacitor. This means when the rotor plates are completely inside of the stator plates it has a capacitance of 350 micromicrofarads. When the rotor plates are turned so that they are all out of the stator plates, the capaci-tance should be about zero. The size of the plates, the number of plates, and the distance the plates are apart de-termine the capacitance.

REVIEW QUESTIONS

1. What are radio frequencies?

2. If a broadcast station states that it is operating on a frequency of 900 kilocycles, what is its frequency in cycles per second?

3. Explain what happens to radio

waves when they hit the Heaviside layer.

4. What is the speed of radio waves?

5. Why is a radio-frequency wave sent out by a transmitter called a carrier wave?

6. What is the purpose of a tuner in a radio receiver?

7. Why will a coil with many turns of wire tune to a lower frequency than a coil with a few turns of wire?

8. What separates the rotor plates and the stator plates in a variable capacitor?

9. Why does a variable capacitor

that has been closed, so that all of the rotor plates are inside of the stator plates, tune to a lower frequency?

10. What is the unit of measure that is used to indicate the capacitance of capacitors?

11. Why are radio-frequency transformers sometimes used in the tuner circuit?

12. Using radio symbols, draw a diagram showing a radio tuner. The radio tuner should be connected to an antenna and a ground. A variable capacitor should be used to tune the circuit.

UNIT 25
HEARING THE RADIO SIGNALS

The Purpose of a Radio Receiver

The radio wave sent out by a broadcast station is a high-frequency wave called a carrier wave because it is carrying the voice frequencies with it. These radio-frequency waves are being changed in strength, or modulated, by the audio waves. If we were to connect a pair of earphones across a radio

tuner and try to listen to a broadcast station, we could not hear anything. The alternating current of the radio waves is so rapid that they could not be heard. The diaphragm of the earphone could not vibrate at all because the current would be changing directions so rapidly. Some method must be used to change the radio waves into sound waves.

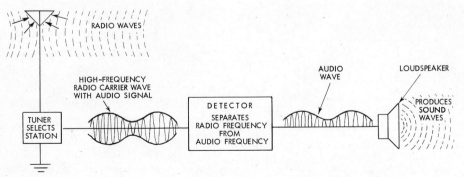

◆ 29. In this block diagram are illustrated the basic principles of radio receiver functioning.

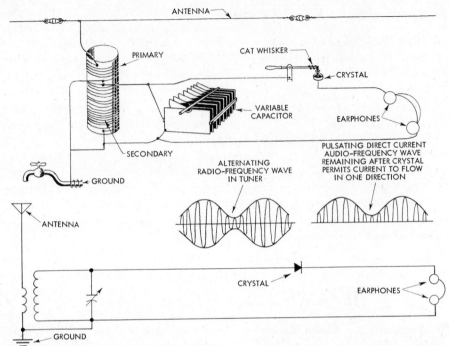

◆ **30. This illustration shows the arrangement of a simple radio receiver called a *crystal set*.**

The purpose of a radio receiver is (1) to tune in a radio station, (2) to separate the audio frequencies from the radio frequencies, and (3) to change the electrical audio vibrations into sound vibrations. See Diagram 29.

The Galena Crystal

One of the simplest types of radio

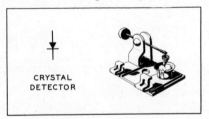

The arrow indicates the direction of easy current-flow.

receivers is the *crystal set*. The crystal is *galena*, a mineral compound of lead and sulfur. It has the ability to permit current to flow in only one direction. Because not all parts of the galena crystal will function properly a fine wire called a "cat whisker" is adjusted to find the sensitive spot.

The Function of the Crystal

The crystal is connected to the tuner as shown in Illustration 30. A pair of earphones is connected in the circuit so that the electrical vibrations can be changed into sound vibrations.

The crystal acts like a one-way valve and will permit the current to flow through it in one direction. Since radio waves are alternating current, that is flowing first in one direction and then in the other direction, the crystal allows the radio current to flow only half of the time. The current that flows through the crystal is a group of direct current pulses. The current that flows through the crystal and then through the earphones is not an alternating current but a *varying direct current.* Illustration 30 shows how this varying direct current still carries with it the audio-frequency wave, including the electrical sound vibrations.

The Earphones

The earphones are constructed very much like the telephone receiver. See Illustration 31. A permanent magnet is used to provide a pull on the thin metal diaphragm. Two sets of electromagnetic coils are connected so that when the current flows through them they can make the diaphragm vibrate.

The varying, or pulsating, direct current that flows through a crystal also flows through the earphone coils. The current through the phones is always flowing in the same direction even though it is pulsating. The varying strength of the radio waves is made by the audio waves. As the current varies

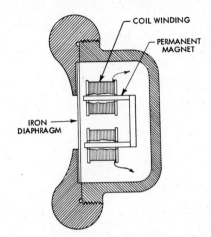

◆ 31. This cross-section view shows the construction of an earphone.

through the earphones, the diaphragm is made to vibrate. The vibrations produced by the earphones are the same as the sound waves that were hitting the microphone in the radio station.

Detection

When a radio circuit, such as the crystal set, is used to separate the radio frequencies from the audio frequencies, it is called a *detector.* Germanium and silicon may also be used as detectors. The advantage of these materials as detectors is that they come in sealed containers and do not need a "cat whisker" to find the sensitive spot.

The Electron Tube as a Detector

One disadvantage of crystal detectors, such as germanium or silicon, is that they cannot increase the strength of the signal. If the signal is not very strong they cannot produce sound through the earphones. The *electron tube* can be used as a detector, and

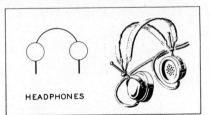

This symbol is the one to use for a double headset.

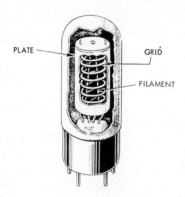

◆ 32. A triode tube has a filament, grid, and plate.

heated until the magnesium is ignited. The magnesium combines with the remaining gases. The silver coating that can be seen inside the glass tubes shows the result of the getter. (The electron tube was originally called *vacuum* tube.)

The two leads from the filament and the other two leads from the grid and plate are then soldered into the prongs on the tube base. The tube base is then cemented to the tube.

it also can be used to increase the strength of the signal.

Construction of an Electron Tube

A simple three-element electron tube is called a *triode*. The triode consists of a filament, a grid, and a plate. See Illustration 32. The *filament,* located in the center of the tube, is made of a thin wire of tungsten that contains a small amount of thorium. Next to the filament is a fine wire in the shape of a coil called the *grid*. The grid is supported by wires, held in the glass stem, so that it does not touch the filament or the plate. The grid is surrounded by a sheet metal rectangle called the *plate*.

Removing the Gases from the Tube

The three elements are sealed inside a glass or metal tube and then all of the air and gases are removed. Since it is very difficult to take all the air and gas out of the tube a *getter* is used. The getter is a small cup of magnesium that is placed inside of the tube. After the air has been removed, the tube is

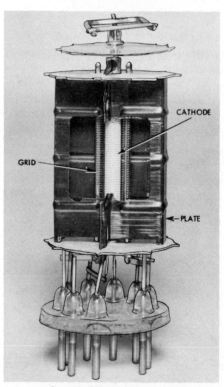

Courtesy Sylvania Electric Products, Inc.

◆ 33. This is a cutaway section of a triode electron tube. The grid surrounds the cathode and the plate encloses both the cathode and the grid.

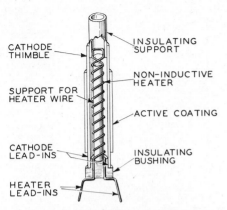

CATHODE THIMBLE

INSULATING SUPPORT

NON-INDUCTIVE HEATER

SUPPORT FOR HEATER WIRE

ACTIVE COATING

CATHODE LEAD-INS

INSULATING BUSHING

HEATER LEAD-INS

◆ 34. Illustration showing the construction of heater-type filament and cathode.

Electron Tubes with a Cathode

In tubes that are to be used with alternating current on the filaments, a specially coated sleeve is placed over the filament. See Illustration 34. This covering over the filament is called the *cathode.* The cathode is not considered an additional element in the tube as it does the work of the filament. A lead from the cathode must also be made to one of the prongs in the tube base.

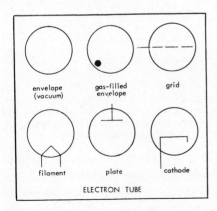

envelope (vacuum)

gas-filled envelope

grid

filament

plate

cathode

ELECTRON TUBE

These elements are combined to form the symbol for any electron tube.

Purpose of the Filament or Cathode

The filament in an electron tube is connected to a low-voltage supply. When the filament heats, electrons are thrown off. Tubes with a filament work best when direct current is connected to them.

In tubes with a cathode the filament is called a *heater* because it heats the cathode. When the cathode gets hot it starts throwing off electrons. Cathode-type tubes are usually used when alternating current is connected to the heater.

The Plate Circuit of a Detector

The plate of an electron tube is connected to a fairly high direct current voltage. Voltages around 90 to 300 volts are very common. Either B batteries or a direct current power supply is used. The earphones are connected

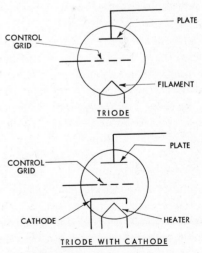

PLATE

CONTROL GRID

FILAMENT

TRIODE

PLATE

CONTROL GRID

CATHODE

HEATER

TRIODE WITH CATHODE

◆ 35. This is how triode tube symbols are drawn.

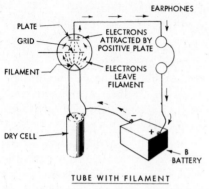

TUBE WITH FILAMENT

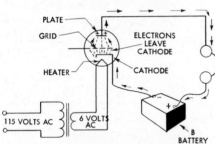

TUBE WITH CATHODE

♦ 36. Arrows show direction of electron flow through an electron tube. Electrons leave the filament and flow to the plate. In a tube with a cathode the electrons leave the cathode and flow to the plate.

to the plate circuit, as in Illustration 36, so that all of the current will flow through them. Since the plate is made positive it will attract the electrons being thrown off the cathode. The electrons that are pulled to the plate flow through the earphones.

The Control Grid

The grid in an electron tube is a coil of wire that is placed between the cathode and the plate. The electrons leaving the cathode must pass between the wires of the grid to get to the plate. If the grid were connected directly to

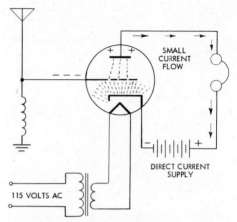

♦ 37. When the grid has lots of electrons they repel some of the electrons that leave the cathode. A small current will then flow to the plate. The diaphragm of the earphones is pulled down very little.

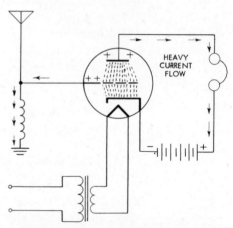

♦ 38. When electrons leave the grid so that the grid is said to have a slight positive charge, a large current flows to the plate from the cathode. The diaphragm of the earphones is pulled down much farther.

the tuner, the alternating current flowing in the tuner would also flow onto the grid. When the grid had lots of electrons on it, these electrons would repel some of the electrons going to the plate. See Diagram 37. This would cut down on the current flow in the plate circuit as fewer electrons would reach the plate.

If the electrons all left the grid, the plate current would increase as the grid would not have a negative charge. See Diagram 38. Any change in the number of electrons on the grid produces a change in the current flowing to the plate. Because the grid affects the plate current this grid is called a *control grid.*

The Tube as a Detector

If the grid were connected directly to the tuner circuit, the alternating current in the tuner would flow onto the grid. The plate current would change very rapidly with alternating current on the grid. This change in the plate current would be so fast that the earphones would not operate. It is necessary to have the tube work like a detector, so that the earphone diaphragm can be made to vibrate with the audio waves.

The *grid leak,* which consists of a capacitor and a resistor connected in parallel, makes it possible for the tube to be a detector. See Diagram 39. The resistor has two million ohms of resistance, and it is called a 2 megohm resistor. *Meg* means one million. The fixed capacitor is a .00025 microfarad capacitor. The grid leak and capacitor are connected between the tuner and the grid. Together they hold enough electrons on the grid so that current flows only one-half of the time in the plate circuit. The tube acts like the crystal set and is a detector. The audio-

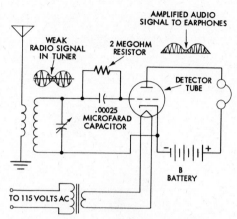

◆ 39. This is a grid leak and capacitor detector.

frequency waves that make up the sound waves are then heard in the earphones.

Why the Electron Tube Increases the Signal Strength

The grid leak and capacitor help the tube operate as a detector. Other than being a detector, the tube also acts like an amplifier and increases the strength of the signal.

When electrons flow on and off the grid the plate current varies. The signal coming to the grid is very

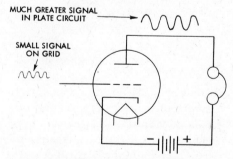

◆ 40. A radio tube amplifies the signal. A very small signal on the grid will produce a large change in plate current.

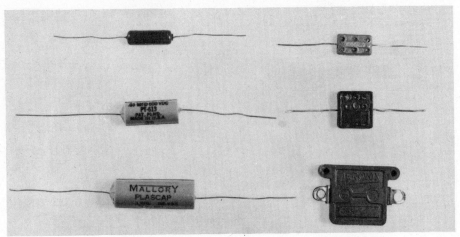

◆ 41. Here are several fixed capacitors. Those on the left are paper capacitors. Those on the right are mica capacitors.

weak. A larger plate current is flowing through the earphones because the plate has a high voltage on it to attract the electrons from the cathode. A very small change of electron flow on the grid produces a large change in plate through the earphones. See Diagram 40.

Fixed Capacitors

Small fixed capacitors (Photograph 41) are made of two metal plates sepa-

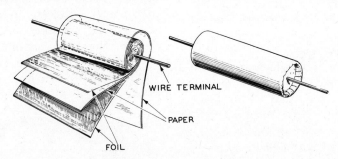

◆ 42. Paper capacitors are made of alternate layers of paper and foil.

current. The changes in plate current are what make the diaphragm of the earphone vibrate.

The electron tube increases the strength of the radio waves because a very small signal on the grid makes a much larger change of current flowing

rated by an insulating material. The most commonly used insulating materials are paper and mica. This insulating material is called the *dielectric*.

In *paper* capacitors (Illustration 42), a layer of paper is placed between two sheets of metal foil that are rolled together. The wire lead on one side of the capacitor goes to one of the metal foils and the wire lead on the other side goes to the other metal foil. The larger the two pieces of metal the greater the capacitance of the capacitor. Paper capacitors usually have the capacitance stamped on the outside.

Mica capacitors (Illustration 43) consist of several layers of metal foil separated by thin sheets of mica. Alternate plates are soldered together. One wire lead goes to one set of plates and another wire lead goes to the other set. The entire capacitor is then placed in

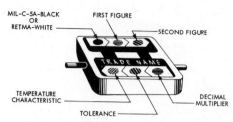

◆ 43. The color code on *mica capacitors* conveys the information indicated.

bakelite to keep out moisture. A group of colored dots, called a *color code,* is usually used to mark the capacitance. As with variable capacitors, the capacitance is given in either microfarads or micromicrofarads.

INTERESTING THINGS TO DO

1. Making a Crystal Diode Radio Receiver.

Materials required:

1 Piece wood, ½" x 4½" x 4½"
1 Piece wood, ½" x 1" x 3½"
1 Spool wire, enamel-covered, No. 24
1 Piece spring brass, ⅜" x 4⅜", 26 gage
1 Piece tubing, brass, ¼" outside diameter (OD), ¾" long
3 Spring clips, Fahnestock, ¾" long
3 Wood screws, RH, steel, ⅜"–6
1 Wood screw, RH, steel, 1¼"–6
1 Washer, brass, No. 6
1 Crystal diode, germanium

Drill a small hole partly through the small wood block ¼" from one end and insert one end of the spool of wire in the hole to hold it in place. Wind 100 turns of wire on the block and secure the other end of the wire by drilling a small hole through the edge of the wood block and passing the wire through it. Shellac or lacquer three sides of the completed coil, but do not lacquer the side on which the slider is to bear. Glue the coil to the wood base.

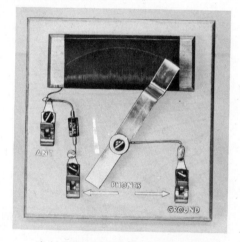

◆ 44. Crystal Diode Radio Receiver

Lay out and drill the piece of spring brass as shown on Drawing 45 and bend it to the shape shown to serve as the contact lever. Secure the contact lever to the wood base with the piece of brass tubing, washer, and long wood screw so that the pointed end will make an arc across the flat side of the

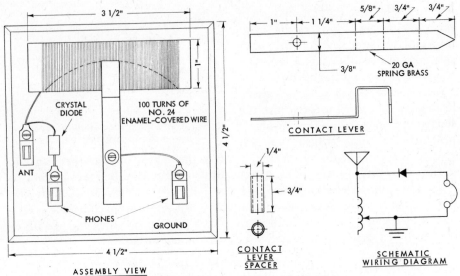

♦ **45. Drawing of Crystal Diode Radio Receiver**

coil. Bear down slightly on the pointed end of the contact lever and move it back and forth across the coil several times to remove the enamel covering from the wire and to permit the lever to make contact with the wire. Secure the Fahnestock clips to the wood base with wood screws and make the connections shown on the drawing. Connect the crystal diode between the antenna clip and one of the phone clips, as shown on the drawing.

Connect a pair of headphones and antenna and ground leads to the proper clips and you should be able to tune in a nearby broadcasting station by moving the contact lever across the coil. A ground connection is usually made by attaching a piece of copper wire to a water pipe and connecting the other end to the "ground" connection on the receiver. The best length of antenna can be determined by trial.

A long antenna will permit the receiver to pick up more stations, but they will be difficult to separate. Choose a length for the antenna that will permit you to receive the largest number of radio stations with little or no interference between them.

2. Capacitor-Tuned Crystal Receiver.

Materials required:

1 Piece wood, 3″ x 5″
1 Variable capacitor, .000365 μf
1 Spool magnet wire, enamel-covered, No. 28
1 Cardboard form, 1″ diameter, 3″ long
1 Crystal detector, cat whisker type
1 Crystal
4 Fahnestock clips

Drill four $\frac{1}{16}$″ holes about $\frac{1}{4}$″ apart and $\frac{1}{4}$″ from one end of the tubing, as shown on Drawing 47. Drill another $\frac{1}{16}$″ hole $\frac{1}{2}$″ from the same end of the tubing and insert one end of the magnet wire through the hole and out

◆ **46. Capacitor-Tuned Crystal Receiver**

through one of the lower holes to hold the wire firmly in place. Wind 100 turns of wire on the cardboard tubing. Drill a $\frac{1}{16}''$ hole close to the winding, pass the end of the winding through the hole, and secure it to one of the holes at the end of the tubing. Drill another $\frac{1}{16}''$ hole $\frac{1}{8}''$ above the first winding and wind 30 turns of wire on the form to serve as the primary winding.

Wind the primary winding in the same direction as the larger coil was wound. Secure the end of the coil in the same manner as the end of the first coil was secured. Cut a circle of wood

so that it will fit into the terminal end of the coil and glue it in place. Secure the coil to the wood base with a wood screw. Secure the detector stand and Fahnestock clips to the wood base and connect the parts together as shown in the schematic diagram, Drawing 47. Instructions on the proper antenna and ground to use with a crystal receiver are given in the section describing the crystal diode receiving set. After a radio station has been tuned in on the receiver the most sensitive spot on the crystal may be found by moving the adjustable arm with the "cat whisker" across the crystal.

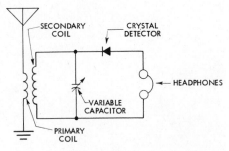

WIRING DIAGRAM

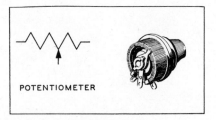

POTENTIOMETER

The potentiometer symbol shows three terminals.

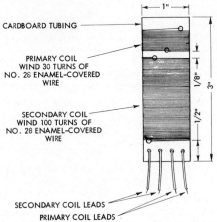

CARDBOARD TUBING

PRIMARY COIL
WIND 30 TURNS OF
NO. 28 ENAMEL-COVERED
WIRE

SECONDARY COIL
WIND 100 TURNS OF
NO. 28 ENAMEL-COVERED
WIRE

SECONDARY COIL LEADS
PRIMARY COIL LEADS

◆ 47. **Drawing for Capacitor-Tuned Crystal Set**

◆ 48. **One-Tube Regenerative Receiver**

3. One-Tube Regenerative Receiver.
Materials required:

1 Antenna coil (see construction details in
 tuned crystal receiver, Drawing 47)
1 Variable capacitor, .000365 µf (C_1)
6 Fahnestock clips
1 Fixed capacitor, mica, .00025 µf (C_2)
1 Resistor, 2,000,000 ohms, ½-watt (R_1)
1 Potentiometer, 10,000 ohms (R_2)
1 6J5 tube
1 Octal tube socket
1 Piece sheet steel, 4″ x 7″, 20 gage
1 Piece masonite, ⅛″ x 1″ x 4″
1 Rubber grommet, ¼″
1 Rubber grommet, ⅜″
2 Pointer knobs

Lay out the piece of sheet steel and
drill holes where shown on Drawing

49. Bend the two ends of the sheet
metal to a 90° angle to form the ends
of the chassis. Secure the capacitor and
coil to the top of the chassis in the
approximate positions shown. Starting
at the bottom end of the coil, count 30
turns of wire upward and solder a connection for the antenna. Secure the
potentiometer in the ⅜″ hole in the
front end of the chassis. Make a terminal strip with a piece of masonite
and Fahnestock clips and secure it to
the back of the chassis. Wire the
receiver as shown in the schematic
diagram.

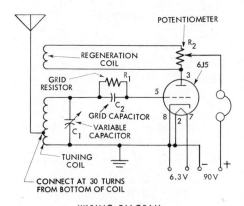

♦ 50. **Wiring underneath the Chassis of the One-Tube Receiver**

WIRING DIAGRAM

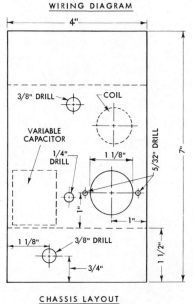

CHASSIS LAYOUT

♦ 49. **Drawing of One-Tube Regenerative Receiver**

When operating the receiver the potentiometer control knob is turned so the receiver is at the most sensitive point without distorting the signals. If the knob is turned too far the music or speech will become unintelligible and a high-pitched squeal will be heard in the headphones. The best operating point is where the receiver is the most sensitive, yet the music or speech is understood clearly. If the receiver fails to produce a high-pitched squeal at any position of the potentiometer knob, the connections between the primary coil and the potentiometer should be reversed.

This receiver will work satisfactorily with batteries or with either of the power supplies described in Unit 27 of this book.

REVIEW QUESTIONS

1. Name the three main purposes of a radio receiver.

2. What happens to alternating current when it is connected to a galena crystal? What is it then called?

3. What kind of current flows through the earphones of a crystal set?

4. Explain the purpose of a detector.

5. Name three types of crystal detectors.

6. Name the three elements in a triode electron tube.

7. What is a "getter" used for?

8. Explain the purpose of a cathode.

9. What effect does the control grid have on the plate current?

10. Draw a diagram of a grid leak detector.

11. How does an electron tube amplify radio signals?

12. How are paper capacitors constructed?

13. What are the main parts of a mica capacitor?

UNIT 26A

RADIO AMPLIFIERS

Importance of the Electron Tube as an Amplifier

The most important advantage of an electron tube is its ability to make radio signals stronger. Many devices

Transformer-Coupled Audio Amplifiers

The signals produced by a detector are not very strong. Usually we like to use a loudspeaker, instead of ear-

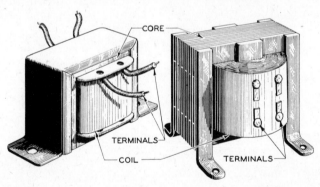

◆ 51. A step-up transformer makes the audio signal stronger.

such as the galena, germanium, and silicon crystals may be used as detectors, but none of these will amplify the signal.

In the electron tube, a very weak signal coming into the control grid can produce a much larger variation of plate current.

phones, so that several people can listen to the receiver at the same time. The audio-frequency signal can be made stronger through the use of another electron tube called an *audio-frequency amplifier*.

One method of coupling the detector to an audio amplifier is to use a

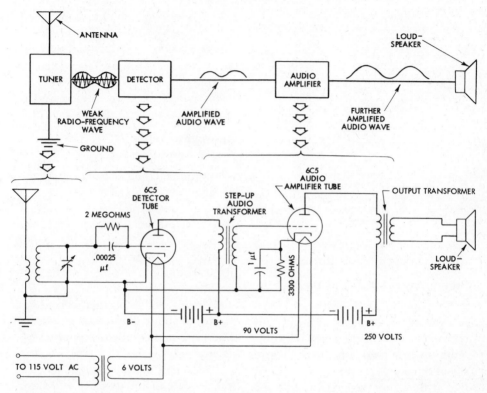

◆ 52. This block diagram and schematic diagram show the arrangement of a tuner, detector, and amplifier.

step-up transformer (Illustration 51). This type of transformer is called an *audio transformer*. The primary of the transformer is connected in the plate circuit in place of the earphones. The secondary is connected to the grid of the audio amplifier as shown in Diagram 52.

When the detector is tuned to a radio broadcasting station the plate of the detector has a varying plate current. This varying plate current is the same as the audio frequencies being sent out by the radio station. These variations in plate current flow through the primary of the transformer. The primary induces a voltage

in the secondary of the transformer. Since it is a step-up transformer, the voltage of the secondary is increased.

The stepped-up voltage from the secondary goes to the control grid of the amplifier tube. Now the grid of the amplifier has a fairly strong audio-frequency signal flowing to it. The audio

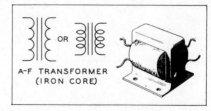

A transformer with a magnetic core is represented like this.

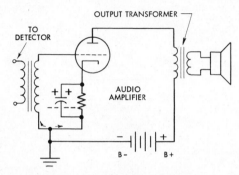

◆ 53. Using a cathode resistor and capacitor to place a small negative voltage on the amplifier grid; this prevents distortion of the signal.

amplifier increases the signal strength enough to operate a loudspeaker.

Preventing Distortion of the Signal

The signal from the detector can provide a very strong alternating current to the grid of the amplifier tube. With such a large variation of grid signal the plate current can be so great that it does not vary exactly like the grid signal. A true signal would not be produced in the loudspeaker. This is called *distorting* the signal. To prevent this distortion, it is necessary to limit the amount of current that can

flow through the tube. A resistor called a *cathode resistor* and a capacitor called a *bypass capacitor* are used for this purpose. They are connected as in Diagram 53. This makes the grid have a small negative voltage, and it is called placing *grid bias* on the tube.

Resistance-Coupled Audio Amplifiers

Another method of connecting the detector to the audio amplifier is called *resistance coupling*. See Diagram 54. A resistor of about 250,000 ohms can be placed in the plate circuit of the detector. Another resistor of about 500,000 ohms can be placed in the grid circuit of the amplifier. To couple these two circuits together a fixed capacitor of about .01 microfarad is used. The capacitor is called a *coupling capacitor*.

The side of the capacitor connected to the plate of the detector will have more or less electrons on it as the plate current changes with the signal. See Diagram 56. The other side of the capacitor will either push electrons on or pull electrons off the grid of the amplifier. Thus the detector is coupled to the amplifier.

Resistance coupling does not pro-

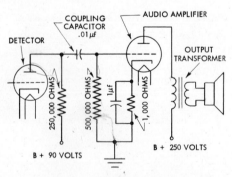

◆ 54. Resistance coupling used to connect detector to an audio amplifier.

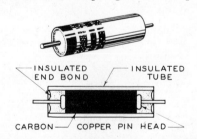

◆ 55. This is a cross-section of a carbon fixed resistor.

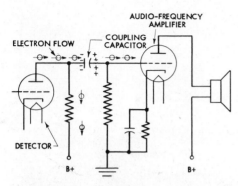

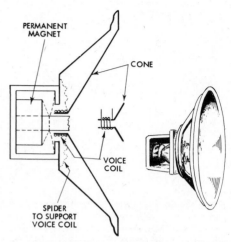

◆ 56. In resistance coupling, a fixed capacitor is used to couple the detector to the audio-frequency amplifier. Changes in electron-flow from the detector plate provide a variation in electron-flow to the coupling capacitor. The grid of the amplifier tube receives its signal through the coupling capacitor.

◆ 57. This is how a permanent-magnet (PM) loudspeaker is constructed.

vide an increase in signal strength as transformer coupling does. All of the amplification must come from the electron tube. It has advantages over the transformer in that it provides very good quality of the audio signal and also it is much cheaper to use.

Loudspeakers

Loudspeakers are used so that sound can be heard some distance away from the radio receiver. A cone is used in the loudspeaker to produce sound waves. As the cone moves back and forth, it moves the air in front and in back of it. This movement of air is what makes the sound waves that we hear.

One of the common types of loud-speakers is called the *permanent magnet speaker* (Illustration 57). A small coil of wire wound on to a hollow tube is glued to the bottom of the cone. This coil is called the *voice coil*. The coil is then placed so that it can move

freely over a pole of a very strong alnico magnet.

A transformer called an *output transformer* is used to couple the amplifier to the speaker. See Illustration 58. Audio-frequency signals flowing in the plate of the amplifier induce a voltage in the secondary of the transformer. These current variations flow through the voice coil. The magnetic field made by the voice coil will pull the cone either in or out of the magnetic field made by the permanent magnet. As the voice coil moves it also causes the cone to move.

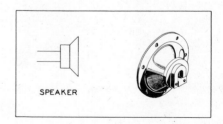

Letter symbols may be added to identify the kind of speaker.

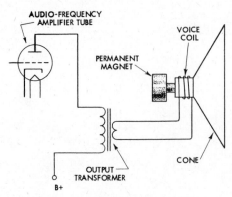

◆ 59B. This is a complete audio amplifier. This type of amplifier can be used as a public address system.

◆ 58. Connecting an output transformer to a permanent-magnet speaker. The secondary of the transformer connects to the voice coil, audio-frequency current flowing through the voice coil makes the cone move in and out, producing sound vibrations.

Uses for Audio Amplifiers

Audio amplifiers have many uses other than in radio receivers. They are used for such purposes as phonograph amplifiers, intercommunications sys-

tems, and public address systems. Several electron tubes may be coupled together to produce the needed volume of sound. See Photograph 59B.

Electron Tubes with Several Elements

Several elements other than the control grid, cathode, and plate are placed in some electron tubes. Tubes with more elements than the triode are called multi-element tubes. Additional elements are placed in some tubes for

◆ 59A. Several kinds of electron tubes are shown here; they are designed to serve a variety of special purposes.

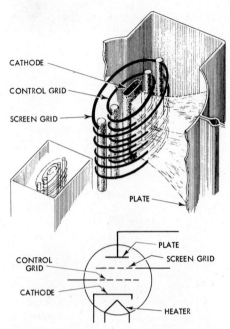

CATHODE

CONTROL GRID

SCREEN GRID

PLATE

PLATE
CONTROL GRID
SCREEN GRID
CATHODE
HEATER

◆ **60. The tetrode tube has four elements.**

special purposes. A *tetrode* is a four-element tube (Illustration 60), and it contains another grid called the *screen grid*. A *pentode* is a five-element tube (Illustration 61) with three grids—a *control grid,* a *screen grid,* and a *suppressor grid*. Sometimes two tubes are placed together in one glass envelope.

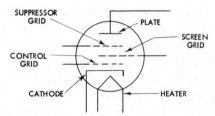

SUPPRESSOR GRID

PLATE

SCREEN GRID

CONTROL GRID

CATHODE

HEATER

◆ **61. There are five elements in a pentode tube.**

All of these tubes have special uses and some require special tube sockets. They look very complicated, but the basic principle of the triode is found in all these tubes.

Radio-Frequency Amplifiers

To increase the radio signals before they reach the detector, an amplifier called a *radio-frequency amplifier* is used. It operates very much like the audio-frequency amplifier except that it amplifies the high-frequency radio signals instead of the low-frequency audio signals. See Diagram 62.

Transformer coupling is usually used to couple the radio-frequency amplifiers together. These transformers are coils like the coils used for the tuner of the detector.

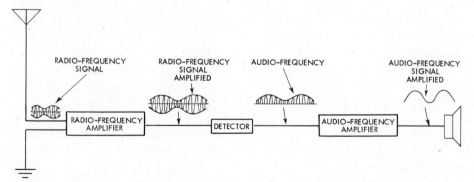

RADIO-FREQUENCY SIGNAL

RADIO-FREQUENCY SIGNAL AMPLIFIED

AUDIO-FREQUENCY

AUDIO-FREQUENCY SIGNAL AMPLIFIED

RADIO-FREQUENCY AMPLIFIER

DETECTOR

AUDIO-FREQUENCY AMPLIFIER

◆ **62. This block diagram shows where a radio-frequency amplifier is used in a receiver circuit.**

One of the important uses for radio-frequency amplifiers is to improve the tuning of the set. Each radio-frequency amplifier can have its own tuner. A variable capacitor is used to tune the circuit. By tuning the amplifier, the receiver can be made to separate the broadcast stations better. Improving the set so that it can easily separate the stations is called making the set more *selective.*

Usually the variable capacitors are connected together so that the radio-frequency amplifiers and the detector are all tuned at the same time. Variable capacitors that are connected together are called *ganged capacitors.*

INTERESTING THINGS TO DO

1. Two-Tube Radio Receiver.
Materials required:

1 Antenna coil
1 Variable capacitor, .000365 μf (C_1)
1 Fixed capacitor, mica, .00025 μf (C_2)
1 Fixed capacitor, .01 μf (C_3)
1 Fixed capacitor, .001 μf (C_4)
1 Electrolytic capacitor, 25 μf, 50 volt (C_5)
1 Fixed resistor, 2,000,000 ohms, $\frac{1}{2}$-watt (R_1)
1 Fixed resistor, 250,000 ohms, $\frac{1}{2}$-watt (R_2)
1 Fixed resistor, 500,000 ohms, $\frac{1}{2}$-watt (R_3)
1 Fixed resistor, 3,300 ohms, 1-watt (R_4)
1 Potentiometer, 10,000 ohms (R_5)
2 6J5 electron tubes
2 Octal sockets
2 Pointer knobs
1 Piece sheet steel, $6\frac{1}{2}$" x $6\frac{1}{2}$", 20 gage
1 Rubber grommet, $\frac{1}{4}$"
1 Rubber grommet, $\frac{3}{8}$"
1 Piece masonite, $\frac{1}{8}$" x 1" x 6"
9 Fahnestock clips

Lay out and drill the piece of sheet steel as shown on Drawing 66. Bend the ends along the broken line to an angle of 90° and mount the tube sockets where shown. Secure the variable capacitor and the antenna coil to the chassis in the approximate positions indicated on the drawing. Place the rubber grommets in the holes in the top of the chassis. Secure the potentiometer in the $\frac{3}{8}$" hole in the front end of the chassis.

Mount the Fahnestock clips to the piece of masonite and secure the com-

◆ 63. A two-tube radio receiver using a regenerative detector and a resistance-coupled audio amplifier.

pleted terminal strip to the back end of the chassis. Mark the terminal strip to show two clips for the antenna and ground, two clips for the loudspeaker, two clips for the 6.3 volt filament supply, and three clips for the two + and − connections. Wire the receiver as shown in the schematic diagram. The same type coil is used with this set as was used in the one-tube receiver described in Unit 25 of this book. If you have not previously built that set, refer to its instructions for the correct coil connections and operating procedure. This receiver will operate with the power supply that is described on pages 230 and 231.

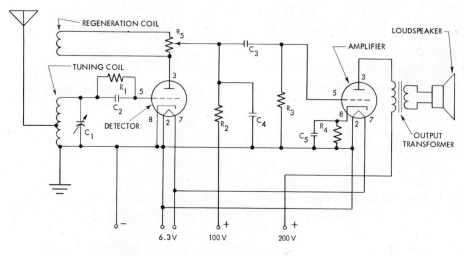

SCHEMATIC DIAGRAM

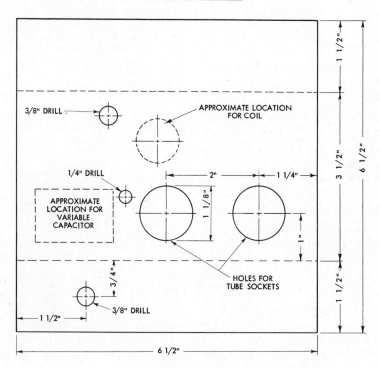

CHASSIS LAYOUT

◆ 64. Drawing of Two-Tube Radio Receiver

REVIEW QUESTIONS

1. Why are audio-frequency amplifiers used?

2. What kind of a transformer is used in a transformer-coupled audio amplifier?

3. Explain why it is important that an electron tube produce a radio signal without distortion.

4. What are the advantages of a resistance-coupled amplifier over the transformer-coupled amplifier?

5. Explain the purpose of the voice coil in a loudspeaker.

6. What is the purpose of the cone in a loudspeaker?

7. What is used to connect the loudspeaker to an electron tube?

8. Name several uses for audio amplifiers.

9. What are electron tubes with more than three elements called?

10. What are the two main purposes of a radio-frequency amplifier?

UNIT 26B
TRANSISTOR FUNDAMENTALS

The Transistor

One of the newest additions to the field of electronics has been the development of the *transistor*. Transistors can be used as amplifiers just like electron tubes. They are now being used in radio receivers, television sets, hearing aids, Geiger counters, transmitters, and in many other places.

The transistor has several advantages over the electron tube. (1) It is very small and takes little space. (2) It does not require a large power supply like the electron tube. Small flashlight

cells will last a long time with transistor circuits. (3) It does not have a heater like the electron tube, so practically no heat is produced. (4) The transistor can take rough handling and not become noisy as some tubes do.

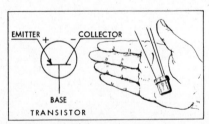

The elements of a transistor are shown this way in a symbol.

◆ 65. Comparing the size of a transistor and a small metal receiving tube.

N-Type Semi-Conductors

Transistors are made from materials called semi-conductors. A semi-conductor is a substance that is not as good a conductor of electricity as metal, but is a better conductor than an insulator. There are a number of semi-conductor materials, but the two most often used in the manufacture of transistors are germanium and silicon. Transistors require semi-conductors with special electrical properties.

Germanium, in its very purest form, is very much like an insulator as it has few electrons which are free to move about. By adding very small quantities of impurities to the germanium, it can be made to conduct electricity. The addition of such impurities as antimony or arsenic to the germanium will increase the number of electrons which are free to move about in the germanium crystal. See Illustration 66A. When a germanium crystal has an excess of "free" electrons, it is called an N-type semi-conductor.

P-Type Semi-Conductors

A second method of making a semi-conductor is by the addition of aluminum or gallium to germanium. When the aluminum or gallium is added to the germanium, a shortage of electrons

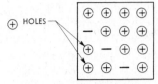

◆ 66b. A P-type semi-conductor has a number of free holes.

is produced in the crystal. Such a semi-conductor is called a P-type semi-conductor; and its usage brings into being a new concept in electricity. This new concept states that a shortage of electrons produces a hole in the semi-conductor. This hole is free to move about much the same as free electrons are in the N-type material. See Figure 66B.

If a battery is placed across the ends of a P-type semi-conductor, a current will flow as shown in Figure 66C. The side of the semi-conductor connected to the positive terminal of the battery will repel the holes in the semi-conductor. The holes which have a positive charge will move toward the negative side of the semi-conductor. The electrons from the negative terminal of the battery flow to the semi-con-

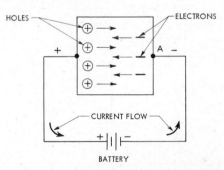

◆ 66c. When a battery is connected across a P-type semi-conductor, current will flow through the material. The holes move toward point A and the electrons move in the opposite direction.

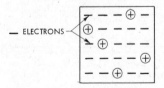

◆ 66a. An N-type semi-conductor has a number of free electrons.

ductor and combine with the positive holes at point *A* of the semi-conductor. When a hole and an electron come together, they combine and neutralize each other. New holes are then formed in the P-type material and these new holes move toward point *A*. As these holes are formed, they release electrons in the semi-conductor and these electrons flow toward the positive terminal of the battery. Thus, a current flows through the semi-conductor.

Forming an N-P Junction

When an N-type and a P-type material are joined together, as in Figure 66D, an area formed between the two semi-conductors is called a junction. If a voltage is applied across the two materials so that the negative terminal of a battery is connected to the N-type semi-conductor and the positive terminal of the battery is connected to the P-type semi-conductor, a current will flow through the circuit.

The holes which are positive in the P-type material will be repelled by the positive terminal of the battery and

will move toward the junction. Likewise, the electrons in the N-type material will be repelled by the negative terminal of the battery and they also will move toward the junction. In the area of the junction, the holes and electrons meet and combine with each other. More electrons from the battery flow into the N-type semi-conductor to replace those electrons that combined with the holes. Also, in the P-type semi-conductor, new holes are created to replace those that were cancelled at the junction. These newly formed holes release electrons which flow toward the positive terminal of the battery.

In the circuit with the negative terminal of the battery connected to the N-type material and the positive terminal connected to the P-type material, current flows through the circuit. Such a circuit produces a current flow that is called *forward bias*.

Reverse Bias on the N-P Junction

Should the battery polarity be reversed as in figure 66E, no current will flow through the circuit. The electrons

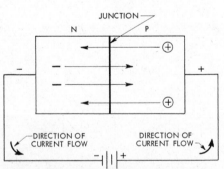

♦ 66d. When a negative charge is applied to the N-type material and a positive charge to the P-type material, a current will flow through the N-P junction.

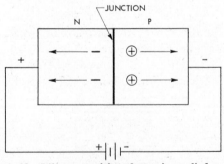

♦ 66e. When a positive charge is applied to the N-type semi-conductor and a negative charge to the P-type semi-conductor, practically no current flows through the N-P junction.

in the N-type material will be attracted to the positive terminal of the battery, and the holes in the P-type material will be attracted to the negative battery terminal. Since both electrons and holes move away from the junction, there is very little opportunity for the holes and electrons to combine. Practically no current will flow in the circuit. When the polarity placed on an N-P junction is such that the N-type material is connected to a positive charge and the P-type material is connected to a negative charge, current will not flow and this is called *reverse bias*.

The N-P Junction is a Detector

The N-P junction semi-conductor will permit current to flow in one direction, but when the polarity across the junction is reversed, current will not flow. If an alternating current is applied to a semi-conductor junction, the output from the semi-conductor will change the AC into pulsating direct current.

When discussing radio receiver detectors, we learned that both the galena crystal and the diode vacuum tube were used to change the alternating radio frequency waves into pulsating direct current. This pulsating direct current made the earphones function to form the sound waves. A semi-conductor junction crystal can be used as a radio receiver detector the same as the diode tube on the galena crystal. Many modern transistor radio receivers use germanium crystals called junction diodes as detectors.

Forming a Junction Transistor

Junction transistors are formed by using three layers of semi-conductor materials placed together like a sandwich as shown in Figure 66F. This is called an N-P-N junction. The two outside semi-conductors are of N-type material, and the center semi-conductor is of P-type material. The center P-type material is called the base. The base is extremely thin and is usually less than .001 inch wide. The N-type material on one side of the base is called the emitter, and the N-type material on the opposite side is called the collector. Leads coming from the transistor are identified as the emitter, the collector, and the base.

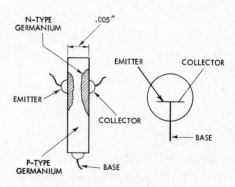

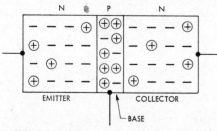

◆ 66f. An N-P-N transistor consists of an N-type emitter, an N-type collector, and a P-type base.

◆ 66g. This illustration shows the construction of a transistor with the diagram of a transistor symbol.

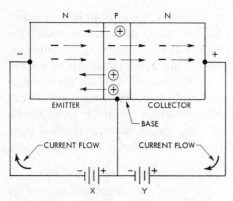

◆ 66h. When the proper voltage is applied to the emitter, base, and collector of an N-P-N transistor, current flows through the entire transistor.

A second type transistor called the P-N-P transistor is similar to the N-P-N except that the base semi-conductor is of the N-type and the emitter and collector is of the P-type.

N-P-N Transistor Action

To understand the fundamental operation of a transistor, we can assume that external batteries are connected to the transistor leads so that current will flow through the transistor. The battery marked X in Figure 66H is connected between the emitter and the base. Since the polarity across the junction is such that N-type material has a negative charge and the P-type material has a positive charge, this is forward bias and current flows through the junction.

If Battery Y in Figure 66H is connected across the collector and the base so that the negative terminal goes to the collector and the positive terminal goes to the base, no current flows. This is reverse bias.

If the collector is connected to the positive terminal of Battery Y, Figure 66H, electrons come through the base and are attracted toward this positive charge and will flow right on through the collector. Because the base is so thin, the electrons which flow from the emitter toward the base actually tend to flow right through it toward the collector. Thus, current flows through the entire transistor.

Applying a Signal to the Emitter

To learn how a transmitter func-

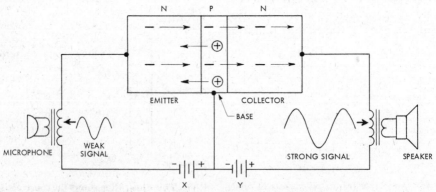

◆ 66i. A weak signal applied to the emitter circuit through the microphone is amplified by the transistor.

tions, we need to apply a signal to the emitter circuit. In Figure 66J a microphone transformer has been placed in the circuit of the emitter and the base. When someone speaks into the microphone, an alternating current appears in the secondary of the transformer. The pure direct current produced by the battery in the emitter circuit is now varied by the AC signal. Since the AC signal is first positive and then negative, the voltage in the circuit is either increased or decreased.

When the signal is positive, it subtracts from the voltage of battery X, and the electron flow through the emitter is reduced. The current flow through the output transformer connected in the collector circuit will also be reduced because electrons from the emitter flow into the base and through the collector. When the input signal becomes negative, the emitter will have an increased voltage, as the negative signal will add to the voltage of battery X. Increasing the current flow in the emitter will also increase the current flow through the output transformer of the collector circuit.

From this illustration we can see that a signal applied to the emitter circuit produces a similar signal in the collector circuit. Thus, the emitter controls the collector current. This action is similar to that found in the vacuum tube where the grid controls the plate current.

Amplification in a Transistor

Because the battery polarity produces forward bias in the emitter cir-cuit, current flows very readily. Since current flows easily, there is very little resistance in the circuit. In the collector and base circuit reverse bias is applied so that very little current flows in this part of the circuit. The collector-base has a fairly high resistance.

When a signal is applied to the emitter, current will flow through the output circuit of the collector. This current will flow even though a very large resistance is placed in the collector circuit. A very small change in emitter voltage will produce a current change in the collector circuit. This changing current is flowing through a large output load resistor. A small current of only a very few milliamperes, when flowing through a large load resistor, can produce a large voltage drop. Using Ohm's law, we know that Voltage = Current times Resistance ($E = IxR$). A transistor amplifies because a small voltage change applied to the emitter circuit will cause a large voltage change in the collector output circuit.

The P-N-P Transistor

A P-N-P transistor can be used for an amplifier the same as the N-P-N. When using the P-N-P transistor, the voltage polarities are opposite to those used on the N-P-N transistor. Figure 66J illustrates how the polarities are connected for the P-N-P transistor.

When wiring transistors in circuits, it is extremely important to know whether P-N-P or an N-P-N is to be used. By using the wrong battery polarities on transistors, they can easily be damaged.

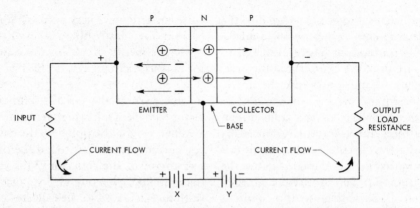

◆ **66j.** In a P-N-P transistor the positive holes in the emitter are repelled by the positive charge placed on the emitter by battery X. The holes flow through the thin base and into the collector. In the collector they combine with the electrons produced by the negative terminal of battery Y. Electrons in the emitter are attracted toward the positive terminal of battery X and new holes are then formed in the emitter.

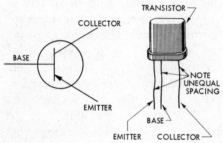

◆ **66k.** A symbol for a P-N-P transistor. The arrow for the emitter points toward the base.

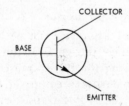

◆ **66l.** A symbol for an N-P-N transistor. The arrow for the emitter points away from the base.

Transistor Circuits

Transistors may be connected into circuits in any one of three ways. These hook-ups, called configurations, are named common-base, common-emit-

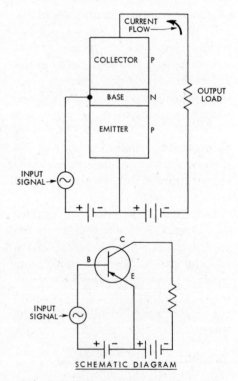

◆ **66m.** A common emitter circuit using a P-N-P transistor.

ter, and common-collector. In each of the circuits one of the electrodes is common to both the input and output circuit.

The circuit most used as a simple amplifier is the common emitter shown in Figure 66M. The signal is applied to the base much like applying a signal to the grid of a vacuum tube.

A simplified circuit of the common emitter which requires only one battery is shown in Figure 66N.

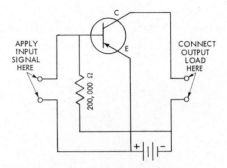

◆ **66n. A typical schematic diagram of an amplifier circuit using a P-N-P transistor.**

INTERESTING THINGS TO DO

1. Transistor Radio Receiver.
Materials Required:

1 Antenna coil (see text)
1 Variable capacitor, .000365 μf (see text) (C_1)
1 Crystal diode, general purpose, G. E. or Sylvania 1N64
1 Fixed capacitor, .02 μf (C_2)
1 Resistor, 220,000 ohms, ½-watt (R)
1 Transistor, Raytheon 722 or G. E. 2N107
2 Pen light cells

This radio receiver may be built by placing the parts on a wood base and using the standard-size parts described with the crystal set in Unit 25 of this book. If you want to build a very small set that you can carry in your pocket,

miniature parts to work with transistors may be obtained from radio mail order companies and wholesale radio houses. Using miniature parts makes it possible to build the complete receiver shown in Schematic Drawing 69 in a plastic box only 1″ deep, 2″ wide, and 3″ long.

To build the receiver in a small space use a Transistor Loop Antenna instead of a standard-size antenna coil. For the standard variable capacitor use a 365 $\mu\mu f$ Super-Midget variable capacitor. The only other substitution will be a miniature-type fixed capacitor for

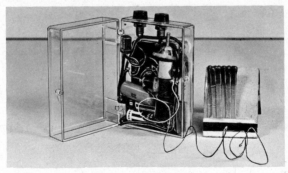

◆ **67. A transistor radio receiver built in a small plastic case. A match folder is next to the receiver.**

the capacitor, C_2. Wire set according to the schematic diagram. Phone tip jacks may be provided for the head-

phones if it is not desired to have the headphones permanently attached to the set.

◆ 68. A soap dish was used to hold this transistor radio receiver. A shaft has been soldered to the padder-type capacitor that is used to tune the receiver.

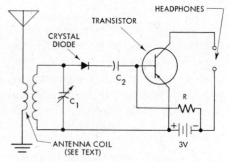

SCHEMATIC DIAGRAM

◆ 69. Schematic Diagram of Transistor Radio Receiver

REVIEW QUESTIONS

1. What is meant by the term semi-conductor?

2. Explain the difference between an N-type and a P-type semi-conductor.

3. How does a free hole differ from a free electron?

4. If current is to flow through an N-P junction, how must the battery polarity be connected to the junction?

5. What is an important use made of the junction diode?

6. Name the three principal parts of a junction transistor.

7. In a complete transistor circuit, what happens in the collector circuit when an AC signal is applied to the emitter?

8. What is the basic difference between an N-P-N and a P-N-P transistor?

9. Why is it extremely important to observe the battery polarities when connecting transistor circuits?

10. Name the most common configuration circuit used with transistors.

UNIT 27
RADIO POWER SUPPLIES

Direct Current for Radio Receivers

Radio receivers always need a source of direct current for the electron tube plate. B batteries can be used for this

purpose, but they must be replaced when worn out. Most radio receivers are made so that they can be plugged into a convenience outlet that has 115-volt alternating current. The alternat-

◆ 70. A small and a large selenium rectifier are shown here. Rectifiers change alternating current into direct current.

ing current is then changed to direct current by the power supply. Power supplies use a *rectifier* to change the alternating current into direct current.

Selenium Rectifiers

Selenium is a chemical material that will permit current to flow through it in one direction. When alternating current starts to flow in the other direction it will stop the electrons from flowing.

A selenium rectifier (Photograph 70) is made of a group of iron washers that have been covered on one side with selenium. The selenium-coated washers are then placed together so that all of the coated sides are facing in the same direction.

Illustration 71 shows how the selenium rectifier is connected in an alternating current circuit. Since it will

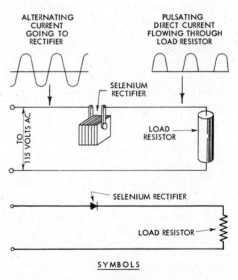

◆ 71. Circuit using a selenium rectifier as a half-wave rectifier. Alternating current is rectified so that current through the resistor is a pulsating direct current. Current flows half of each cycle.

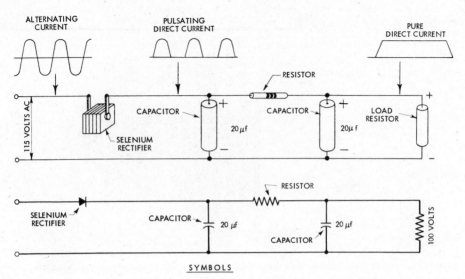

◆ 72. **Half-wave selenium rectifier and filter circuit. Capacitors and resistor filter pulsating direct current so that a pure direct current is available at the output.**

permit the current to flow in one direction and not in the other direction, a pulsating direct current will flow through the resistor. This type of rectifier is a *half-wave* rectifier as it produces a direct current during half of the alternating current cycle. No current flows during the other half of the cycle.

Filtering the Pulsating Direct Current

The pulsating direct current coming out of the rectifier would not work on the plate of an electron tube. The plate current would be changing with each of the pulses. A constant direct current without any variations is necessary for the electron tube power supply.

It is necessary to smooth out the pulsating direct current and make it a pure direct current. Smoothing of the

current is done through the use of a *filter.*

The filter consists of two fixed capacitors and a resistor connected as in Illustration 72. These capacitors are very large ones having a capacitance of 20 microfarads or more. When the current flows through the filter, the capacitors become charged and store large quantities of electrons. As soon as the current stops flowing from the rectifier the capacitors furnish electrons to the circuit. Thus the capacitors tend to provide a constant flow of electrons to the radio receiver.

Each time the current flows through the rectifier a surge of electrons flows through the filter. The resistor is used to try to stop these sudden surges of electrons. Through the use of the resistor and the capacitors, a constant direct current is made available for the radio receiver.

◆ 73. The small silicon rectifier on the left will handle as much current as the vacuum tube rectifier on the right.

Filter Capacitors

Capacitors used in filters are usually electrolytic capacitors. These capacitors have plates made of aluminum separated by an aluminum oxide dielectric. Electrolytic capacitors are used because a large capacitance can be obtained in a small container. Sometimes several capacitors are placed together in one container.

All electrolytic capacitors have positive and negative terminal markings. It is very important to connect the positive terminal to the positive side of the rectifier circuit and the negative terminal to the negative side of the circuit. Very often the negative side of the filter is connected to the ground that is the frame of the power supply.

Silicon Rectifiers

One of the most recent developments in the field of semi-conductors has been the use of silicon diodes as power supply rectifiers. A silicon diode consists of a P-N junction much like that used in a transistor. The P-type material has small amounts of aluminum added to the silicon and the N-type material has phosphorus added to the silicon. When an alternating current is applied to the diode, current will flow in one direction through the diode but will not flow in the opposite direction.

The silicon rectifiers have many advantages over other type rectifiers, and because of these advantages they are being used to replace old type rectifiers. These advantages include having a very high operating efficiency with little voltage loss, and being so small that they are often used in places where space is an important factor. In addition, their ability to handle high currents makes silicon diodes very popular as rectifiers.

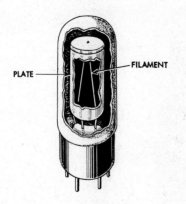

◆ **74. A diode is a two-element electron tube.**

Diode Electron Tube Rectifiers

Two-element electron tubes called *diodes* (Illustration 74) are used as half-wave rectifiers. The diode consists of a filament and a plate. A transformer is used to step up the voltage for the high-voltage supply, to provide filament voltage for the rectifier tube, and, also, to supply the heater voltage for the radio receiver tubes. See Diagram 75.

Alternating current flows through the secondary windings. When the plate of the diode tube is positive, it attracts the electrons being thrown off by the filament. Electrons flow through the tube from the filament to the plate and through the transformer. These electrons return to the filament through the load resistor. The filament is then the positive terminal for the power supply, and the high-voltage transformer lead is the negative terminal.

As the alternating current changes the direction of electron flow, the plate

becomes negative and no current flows through the tube. Since current flows through the tube during only half of the alternating current cycle, the diode produces a pulsating direct current. Pulsating direct current from the half-wave rectifier cannot be used to operate a receiver until it has been filtered.

Full-Wave Electron-Tube Rectifiers

Half-wave rectified current is hard to smooth out because one-half of the time no current is flowing. The filter must be able to provide current during the time when the rectifier is not in operation. Rectifiers that rectify both of the alternating current cycles so that a more constant flow of current is available are often used. These rectifiers are *full-wave* rectifiers.

An electron tube for full-wave rectifiers uses two diodes in one glass envelope. Usually 250 volts or more are needed for a radio receiver power supply. The high-voltage secondary of

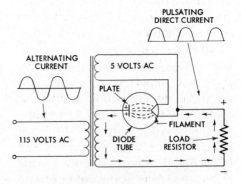

◆ **75. Half-wave rectifier using a diode electron tube. When plate is positive it pulls electrons from the filament and current flows through the tube. No current flows when plate is negative.**

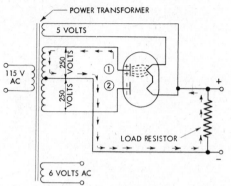

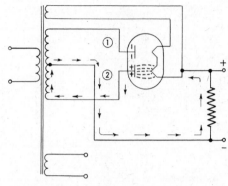

◆ 76. When plate *1* is positive, plate *2* is negative. Electrons flow from filament to plate *1* and out through the center tap of the transformer.

◆ 77. When plate *2* is positive electrons are pulled to it. Electrons flow out through the center tap of the transformer. Both cycles of alternating current are rectified.

the transformer is tapped in the center. Each side of the center connection produces 250 volts.

The double-diode tube has two plates and two filaments. One plate goes to one side of the high-voltage winding, and the other plate goes to the other side of the winding. See Diagrams 76 and 77.

When plate 1 is positive it pulls the electrons from the filament and current flows through that part of the tube. As the alternating current starts to flow the other direction, plate 1 becomes negative and plate 2 becomes positive. Now current flows through plate 2 out through the center tap. The electron flow through the center tap is always in the same direction. The direct current pulses flowing through the load resistor look like Illustration 78. Current is flowing almost all of the time, but it is still necessary to have a filter system.

Filters with a Choke Coil

A much improved filter system can be made using a *choke coil* instead of a resistor. Most power supplies use a choke. The choke is very much like one winding of a transformer since it is made of many turns of wire wrapped around a laminated iron core. The choke is better than the resistor because it provides better filtering and does not cut down the voltage as much as the resistor does. See Diagram 79.

The choke coil tries to keep a steady current flowing. It can be compared to a flywheel in an engine that keeps the engine turning over at a constant

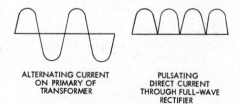

ALTERNATING CURRENT
ON PRIMARY OF
TRANSFORMER

PULSATING
DIRECT CURRENT
THROUGH FULL-WAVE
RECTIFIER

◆ 78. Illustration showing full-wave rectifier current flow.

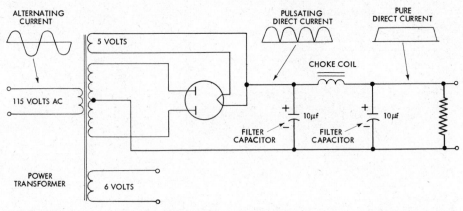

ALTERNATING CURRENT

PULSATING DIRECT CURRENT

PURE DIRECT CURRENT

5 VOLTS

CHOKE COIL

115 VOLTS AC

+ 10μf   + 10μf

FILTER CAPACITOR   FILTER CAPACITOR

POWER TRANSFORMER

6 VOLTS

◆ 79. **Full-wave rectifier with a filter. The filter uses a choke coil and two capacitors to change pulsating direct current to pure direct current.**

speed. The choke helps in smoothing out the pulsating direct current. A choke coil, like any coil, is called an *inductance.* The unit of inductance is the *henry.* Chokes with from 4 to 30 henries are used in power supplies.

A full-wave rectifier does not require as much filter as a half-wave rectifier. Smaller filter capacitors can be used. Capacitors with a capacitance of about 10 microfarads are most common.

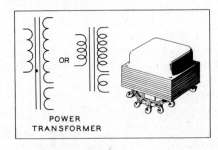

OR

POWER TRANSFORMER

The symbol shows how a power transformer may supply different voltages.

INTERESTING THINGS TO DO

1. Half-Wave Selenium Power Supply.

Materials required:

1 Piece sheet steel, 5″ x 3″, 20 gage
1 Power transformer (*T*), primary 117 volts, secondary 125 volts, center tap (CT), 6.3 volts. (Stancer PA–8421 or Thordarson T26R32)
1 Selenium rectifier, 50 milliampere (MA)
1 Electrolytic capacitor, dual, 20–20 μf, 150 volts (C_1, C_2)
1 Resistor, 1-watt, 33 to 100 ohms (R_1)
1 Resistor, 5-watt, 10,000 ohms (R_2)
1 Resistor, 5-watt, 20,000 ohms (R_3)
1 Toggle switch (optional)
1 Four-point terminal strip
1 Rubber grommet, ⅜″
1 Line cord and plug cap

Hook-up wire

This power supply is easy to build and requires fewer parts than a regular full-wave supply. Its power output is sufficient to operate either of the radio receivers which are described in the preceding units of this book.

Lay out and drill the piece of sheet steel as shown on Drawing 81. Bend each end of the sheet along the broken lines to form a 90° angle. Secure a rubber grommet in the hole on top of the chassis. Mount the selenium rectifier and the power transformer about

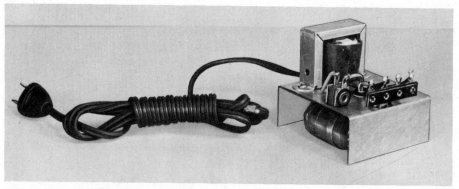

◆ 80. A half-wave selenium power supply. This power supply can be used on the one- and two-tube radio receivers.

where shown on the drawing. Since the mounting holes will vary with different makes of transformers and rectifiers, no holes are shown. Mount the dual capacitor, C_1 and C_2, and the resistors, R_1, R_2, and R_3, beneath the chassis and bring the leads up through the rubber grommet. Resistor, R_1, is merely to protect the selenium rectifier from sudden voltage surges from the capacitor and may have any resistance of from 33 to 100 ohms.

Secure the terminal strip to the top of the chassis and connect the power leads to it as shown on the schematic diagram. Mark the terminal strip so that it will show the voltage between each pair of terminals. The power supply may be controlled either at the supply line outlet or with a toggle switch. If a switch is desired, drill a $\frac{3}{8}''$ hole in one side of the chassis and connect the switch in the transformer side of the power line, as shown on the schematic diagram. Connect the line cord and plug to the transformer and the power supply is ready to operate.

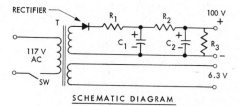

SCHEMATIC DIAGRAM

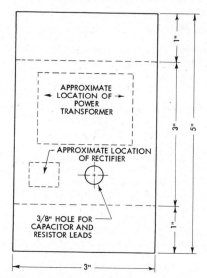

CHASSIS LAYOUT

◆ 81. Drawing of Half-Wave Selenium Power Supply

◆ 82. A full-wave power supply using a power transformer and rectifier tube.

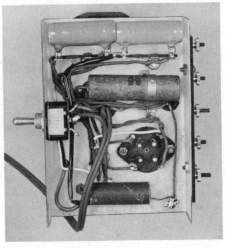

◆ 83. Wiring underneath the Chassis of the Power Supply

2. Full-Wave Rectifier.

Materials required:

1 Power transformer, 450 volts, CT, 50 MA, 5-6.3–volts (T)
1 Choke coil, 6-henry, 50 MA
1 Capacitor, electrolytic, dual 20 μf, 450 volts (C_1, C_2)
1 Capacitor, electrolytic, 4 μf, 450 volts (C_3)
2 Resistors, 20,000 ohms, 10-watt
1 Rectifier tube, 80
1 Tube socket
1 Toggle switch, single-pole
1 Rubber grommet, 3/8″
1 Rubber grommet, 1/2″
1 Piece masonite, 1/8″ x 2″ x 5″
5 Fahnestock clips·
1 Line cord and plug cap
1 Piece sheet steel, 6″ x 7″, 20 gage

Lay out and drill the piece of sheet steel as shown on Drawing 84. Bend the ends along the broken lines to an angle of 90°. Mount the choke coil and the power transformer on the top of the chassis in the approximate positions shown on the drawing. Place the toggle switch in the 3/8″ hole in the front end of the chassis. Make a ter-minal strip with the piece of masonite and Fahnestock clips and secure it to the back end of the chassis. Secure the electrolytic capacitors and the two resistors underneath the chassis.

Wire the power supply as shown in the schematic diagram. The two resistors connected in series serve to keep the high voltage of the power supply at a constant value and to provide a means of getting an additional lower voltage. The voltage across the output of the power supply will be approximately 200 volts, and since the two resistors connected across the output have the same resistance, the voltage between the point where they are connected together and the negative terminal will be approximately 100 volts. Mark the terminals on the terminal strip so that the output voltages may be easily identified.

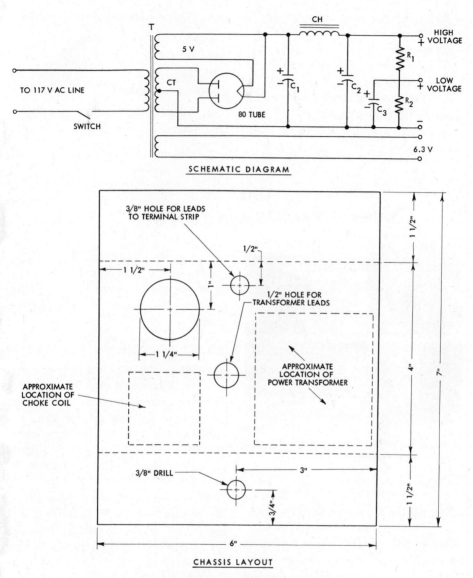

SCHEMATIC DIAGRAM

CHASSIS LAYOUT

◆ 84. Drawing of Full-Wave Power Supply

REVIEW QUESTIONS

1. Why is direct current needed for radio receivers?

2. What kind of current is produced by a half-wave rectifier?

3. Explain the purpose of a filter.

4. What does the capacitor do in a filter system?

5. Why are electrolytic capacitors used in filter systems?

6. What are the elements found in a diode electron tube?

7. When a single diode is used, what is that kind of rectifier called?

8. Explain the advantages of a full-wave rectifier.

9. How many diodes are needed in a full-wave rectifier?

10. What is the purpose of a choke in a filter?

UNIT 28

ELECTRONIC DEVELOPMENTS

Courtesy San Diego City Schools

◆ 85. A television camera being used in a station studio.

The Television Camera Tube

Television has been one of the greatest inventions in the field of electronics. The ability to send pictures through the air waves and to make these pictures visible in a television receiver is a wonderful development.

A television station has two transmitters sending out high-frequency radio waves. See Diagram 86. One transmitter sends out the sound signals, and the other sends out picture signals. The picture signals are first picked up by a television camera. The camera uses a tube that is sensitive to light like the photoelectric cell. This tube changes light into a flow of electrons.

It is not possible to send a complete picture. It is necessary to break the picture up into a group of tiny parts of light. A beam of electrons called a *scanning beam* is made to move across the picture picking up the light received by the camera. The beam starts at the top of the picture and goes from one side to the other to the bottom of the picture.

This scanning beam sweeps across the picture and breaks it up into 525 lines. Each complete picture is made up of particles of light found in the 525 lines. It takes $\frac{1}{30}$ of a second for a picture to be completed; thus, 30 pictures are sent out every second. See Illustration 87.

The Television Transmitter

The electron flow from the camera is then made stronger by an amplifier called a *video amplifier*. These picture

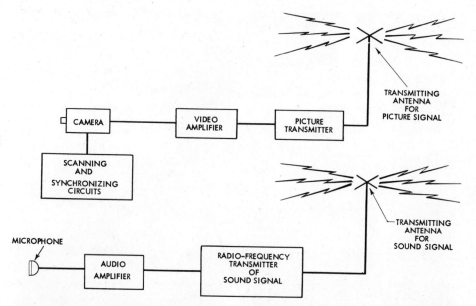

◆ 86. A block diagram of a television transmitting station. One transmitter sends out the picture signal and the other transmitter sends out the sound signal.

waves are combined with the high-frequency carrier of the transmitter. A transmitting antenna then sends these waves out into the air.

Television signals travel in a straight line like a beam of light. For this reason transmitting antennas are placed in as high a location as possible so that the signals can cover a fairly large area. See Illustration 90.

Frequency Modulation

In a standard broadcast station the sound waves and the carrier wave are combined so that the carrier wave is increased and decreased in strength by the sound waves. This is called *amplitude modulation*. Television uses another method of combining the sound waves and the carrier wave called

◆ 87. A drawing of the scanning lines of a picture picked up by a television camera. Each picture takes 1/30 of a second to complete and it is made up of 525 lines. Two sets of lines are used to make the 525 lines of the picture. The beam scans half of the lines (262½) as shown by the solid line. Then it starts back again between the first lines and scans the other 262½ lines as shown by the broken lines.

START OF FIRST 262 1/2 LINES

START OF SECOND 262 1/2 LINES

Courtesy Radio Corporation of America

◆ 88. This high-power television station has an ultra-high-frequency transmitter with a radiated power of one million watts.

Courtesy Bell Systems

frequency modulation. In frequency modulation the sound waves vary the frequency of the carrier as shown in Illustration 91.

Frequency modulation is also used in ultra-high-frequency broadcast stations called *F M* stations. The main advantage of using frequency modulation is that noises made by such things as electrical circuits in the home, lightning, and automobile ignition are not

◆ 89. Radio relay stations and towers, spaced about 30 miles apart, provide a line-of-sight route over which telephone calls and television programs can be relayed great distances. The radio waves that do the work are of super-high frequencies and travel in fairly straight lines, like a beam of light.

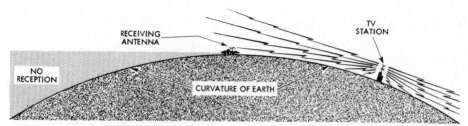

◆ 90. Television signals travel in a straight line like a beam of light, so antennas are made as high as possible.

heard in the receiver. Also, better sound quality is possible through the use of frequency modulation.

The Television Receiver

The television receiver has a tuner that is used to select the various stations. It tunes in both the sound signal and the picture signal. Since both the sound and the picture signals are on slightly different frequencies, they are separated in the receiver. The sound signal is amplified and is heard from the loudspeaker. The picture signal is amplified and is seen on the picture tube.

The Cathode-Ray Tube

The picture tube is called a *cathode-ray tube*. It is the face of the cathode-ray tube that we see when we look at a television set. Inside the face of the tube there is a coating of a material that will glow when electrons strike it. The stronger the flow of electrons the more the tube will light up. This glow from the electrons hitting the face of the tube is what makes up the black and white of the picture.

The picture tube is adjusted so that the beam of electrons can keep in step

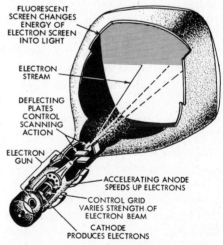

◆ 92. The video wave is picked up by your television receiver, and fed into a picture tube, or *kinescope*. There it varies the strength of a stream of electrons. As the electron stream plays across the fluorescent screen at the wide end of the tube, it paints the same picture seen by the camera.

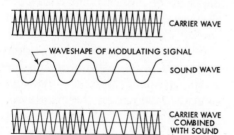

◆ 91. In frequency modulation the carrier is varied in *frequency* by the sound waves, while the amplitude remains unchanged.

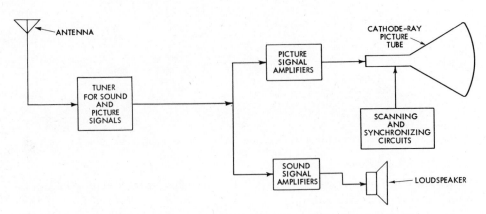

◆ 93. This simplified block diagram shows fundamental arrangement of a television receiver.

with the beam in the television camera. Special circuits, called synchronizing circuits, keep the beam of the television camera and the beam of the cathode-ray tube together. As in the camera, the cathode-ray tube beam must move across the face of the tube making 525 lines 30 times per second. This means that the electron beam is traveling 15,750 times per second across the face of the screen. As the beam moves across the screen, it paints the picture that the camera is picking up.

Color Television

A color television transmitter uses three camera tubes for the picture signal. Each camera picks up a different color from the scene being broadcast. One camera selects the red light from the scene, the second camera selects the green, and the third camera selects the blue light. These three color signals are all sent out by the transmitter. Combinations of these color signals are used for the brightness of the picture and also provide a black and white picture for black and white television receivers.

The tube in a color television receiver contains three electron guns which shoot the red, green and blue signals against the face of the tri-color picture tube. The inner face of the tube is coated with many thousands of dots of red, green, and blue phosphors which glow when the electron beam hits them. A screen that has the same number of openings as there are colored dots is located next to the phosphor face inside the picture tube. The holes in the screen are placed so that the beam of electrons sent out by the electron gun that makes up the red part of the picture can hit the red phosphor; the beam that makes up the green part of the picture can hit the green phosphor; and the electrons from the blue part of the picture can hit the blue phosphor. Since the color dots are so small and so close together, your eye brings them together into a true-to-life picture.

◆ 94. Airborne radar enables pilots to peer deep into thunderstorms, detecting areas where rough air may be encountered. Dotted lines on radar scope in cockpit show possible corridors pilot can follow for smooth flight through storm which appears solid to unaided eye.

Radar

Radar is an electronic development made during World War II that has been put to very valuable use during peacetime. In navigation, both at sea and in the air, radar plays a most important part.

You are familiar with an echo of your voice. The sound waves hit a cliff or building and bounce back. You heard your voice when you spoke, and you hear it again when it returns from the cliff or wall that it has hit. This is what happens in radar except that high-frequency radio waves are used instead of sound waves. The radar set sends out a radio wave that strikes an

Courtesy United Air Lines

object and receives the same wave when it returns. The set then performs its most important duty by automatically showing the distance that the object is from the radar set. See Illustration 95.

For example, an airplane can determine its height above the ground through the use of radar. A transmitter is used to send out a radio wave. The signal is beamed toward the ground.

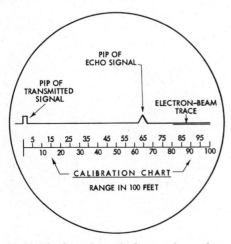

PIP OF
ECHO SIGNAL

PIP OF
TRANSMITTED
SIGNAL

ELECTRON-BEAM
TRACE

5   15   25   35   45   55   65   75   85   95
10   20   30   40   50   60   70   80   90   100

CALIBRATION CHART

RANGE IN 100 FEET

◆ 95. The face of a cathode-ray tube used on a radar screen. The two pips, on the screen, show the distance between the original transmitted signal and the echo signal after it bounced back to the receiver. By using the calibrated scale below the beam, it is possible to determine the distance that the object is away from the radar station.

After it strikes the ground it bounces back up to the airplane. The wave that bounces back is picked up by a radio receiver that is connected to a cathode-ray tube. The signal sent out by the transmitter shows on the screen of the tube by a little bump called a *pip*. The signal that bounced back from the ground also shows on the screen by a pip. It only takes a fraction of a second for these radio waves to go to the ground and bounce back. The time between pips can be calibrated in distance since the speed of radio waves is known to be 186,000 miles per second. By looking at the scale on the front of the tube, it is possible to measure the distance between pips to determine the distance of the airplane from the ground.

Radar is used in many ways. Ships at sea can get a picture of the shore line near them with radar. Other objects in the air or at sea can be located by radar. More and more the principle of

Courtesy Convair

◆ 96. Radio-controlled guided missiles shown aboard a Navy ship. The development of these devices depends upon electronics.

radar is being used for navigation purposes to make air and sea travel safe.

Radio-Controlled Rockets

Rockets and airplanes can be controlled through the use of radio waves. Rockets, or guided missiles, fired into the sky carry a radio receiver with them. The transmitter from the home station sends out radio signals that are picked up by the receiver in the rocket. All of the direction controls in the rocket are connected so that they can be moved by signals coming into the receiver. A radar station watches the rocket. It keeps the operators informed as to the speed and location of the missile. In this way the operators have complete control of the flight of the rocket.

High-altitude research rockets carry transmitters with them. These transmitters inform the ground stations as to how the rocket is performing. Information regarding air pressure, temperature, and other important facts is sent out by the rocket transmitter.

Geiger Counters

One type of instrument used to locate radioactive materials is a *Geiger counter.* When the Geiger tube is brought near uranium ore or other radioactive items, it will make an indicating device operate. The indicator can be a clicking in the earphones, a flashing neon light, or a swinging meter needle.

The most important part of the counter is the small Geiger tube. This glass tube is filled with a gas and has two metal plates, called *electrodes,* inside of it. When radioactive materials are placed near the tube, rays from the material start a current flowing between the plates in the tube. An amplifier is then used to amplify the current flow. The stronger the radioactivity, the stronger the indication on the counter. Faster clicks are heard in the earphones, the neon flashers speed up, or the meter needle moves farther.

Geiger counters have many important uses. Prospectors use them to locate uranium ore deposits. In places where radioactive materials are being used, the Geiger counter can determine whether or not the people or their clothing have come in contact with these dangerous rays.

◆ 97. Using a Geiger counter to locate uranium-bearing ore. In the field these units are usually operated with small flashlight cells.

INTERESTING THINGS TO DO

◆ **98. The Neon Lamp Flasher**

1. Neon Lamp Flasher.
Materials required:

1 Neon lamp, Type Ne–2
1 Fixed resistor, ½-watt (see text)
1 Fixed capacitor, 150 volts (see text)

Many pieces of industrial equipment use a timing circuit similar to the one shown in Diagram 99 to turn an electrical circuit on or off. With its use extremely accurate timing may be obtained whether the time intervals are a fraction of a second or many minutes apart. The timing is governed by the values of the resistor measured in ohms and capacitor measured in farads. If we multiply the value of the resistor by the capacitance of the capacitor in farads, the product will be the time interval in seconds at which the neon lamp will flash.

The flasher shown in Photograph 98 is arranged to flash at one second intervals by using a 1,000,000-ohm resistor and a 1 μf capacitor. The term

farad represents such a large value that it is seldom used in electronic circuits, but since 1,000,000 microfarads equal one farad, we can see that one microfarad can be expressed as .000001 farad. If we wish to increase the timing interval we have only to increase the value of the resistor or the capacitor, so that when both are multiplied together, the product will be the desired timing in seconds.

The input terminals should be connected to a source of direct current, 90 to 135 volts. If it is desired only to observe the flashing rate, a piece of wire should be connected across the output terminals. If it is desired to control another circuit, connect a sensitive relay across the output terminals.

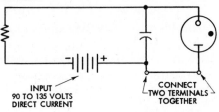

INPUT
90 TO 135 VOLTS
DIRECT CURRENT

CONNECT
TWO TERMINALS
TOGETHER

NEON FLASHER CIRCUIT

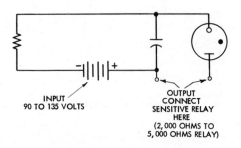

INPUT
90 TO 135 VOLTS

OUTPUT
CONNECT
SENSITIVE RELAY
HERE
(2,000 OHMS TO
5,000 OHMS RELAY)

NEON LAMP CONTROL CIRCUIT

◆ **99. Diagrams of the Neon Lamp Flasher and Control Circuit**

◆ 100. Transistor Code-Practice Oscillator.

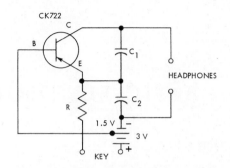

◆ 101. Wiring Diagram of the Transistor Code-Practice Oscillator.

2. Transistor Code Practice Oscillator.

Materials required:

1 Piece wood, ½" x 3" x 3"
1 Transistor, G. E. 2N107 or Raytheon CK 722
2 Fixed capacitors, .01 µf (C_1, C_2)
1 Resistor, 47,000 ohms (R)
2 Pen light cells
4 Fahnestock clips

This transistor oscillator provides a very compact set with which you may learn the radiotelegraph code to qualify for an amateur radio license. Mount the parts in the approximate positions on the wood base as shown in Photograph 100. Wire the set according to Schematic Diagram 101. Two of the Fahnestock clips should be marked "key" and two should be marked "phones." If all of the connections have been made correctly, a high-pitched buzz should be heard in the phones when the key is pressed. For the best results the phones should have an impedance of 2,000 or more ohms. To reduce current drain from the pen light cells, the headphones should be disconnected from the oscillator when it is not in use.

REVIEW QUESTIONS

1. Why are two transmitters used in a television station?

2. How many complete pictures are sent out every second by a television station?

3. Each picture is divided into how many scanning lines?

4. Why is it necessary for a television antenna to be located as high as possible?

5. What is the picture tube in a television receiver called? Explain how it works.

6. Explain how a radar set tells the height that an airplane is from the ground.

7. How can radar be used to make airplane travel safer?

8. What is the advantage of having radio-controlled rockets?

9. For what is a Geiger counter used?

BASIC ELECTRICAL FORMULAS

Ohm's Law

Ohm's law can be used for three different purposes:

To find the current $I = \dfrac{E}{R}$

To find the voltage $E = I \times R$

To find the resistance $R = \dfrac{E}{I}$

Resistances in Series

The total value of resistances connected in series is the sum of the individual resistances.

$$R_{total} = R_1 + R_2 + R_3 + \text{ etc.}$$

EXAMPLE:

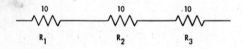

$$R_t = 10 + 10 + 10$$
$$= 30 \text{ ohms.}$$

Resistances in Parallel

In parallel circuits several paths are provided for the flow of current. The total resistance is therefore *less* than that of any individual resistance and is found by means of the following formula.

$$\frac{1}{R_{total}} = \frac{1}{R_1} + \frac{1}{R_2} + \frac{1}{R_3} + \text{ etc.}$$

EXAMPLE:

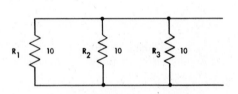

$$\frac{1}{R_t} = \frac{1}{10} + \frac{1}{10} + \frac{1}{10}$$

$$\frac{1}{R_t} = \frac{3}{10}$$

$$3R_t = 10$$

$$R_t = 3.33 \text{ ohms.}$$

Resistances in Series-Parallel

When resistances are connected in series-parallel the effective values of the different parts of the circuit are first separately calculated, so as to form a simple series problem. The equivalent values are then added to the other resistances in the series.

EXAMPLE:

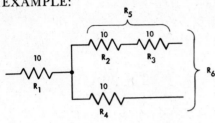

$R_5 = R_2 + R_3$

$\quad = 10 + 10$

$\quad = 20$ ohms.

$\dfrac{1}{R_6} = \dfrac{1}{R_5} + \dfrac{1}{R_4}$

$\quad = \dfrac{1}{20} + \dfrac{1}{10}$

$\quad = \dfrac{3}{20}$

$3R_6 = 20$

$R_6 = 6.66$ ohms.

$R_t = R_1 + R_6$

$\quad = 10 + 6.66$

$\quad = 16.66$ ohms.

Electrical Power

Basic watt formula

Watts = Voltage $\times$ Current

Using symbols

$W = E \times I$

$I = \dfrac{W}{E}$

$E = \dfrac{W}{I}$

STANDARD SYMBOLS FOR ELECTRONICS

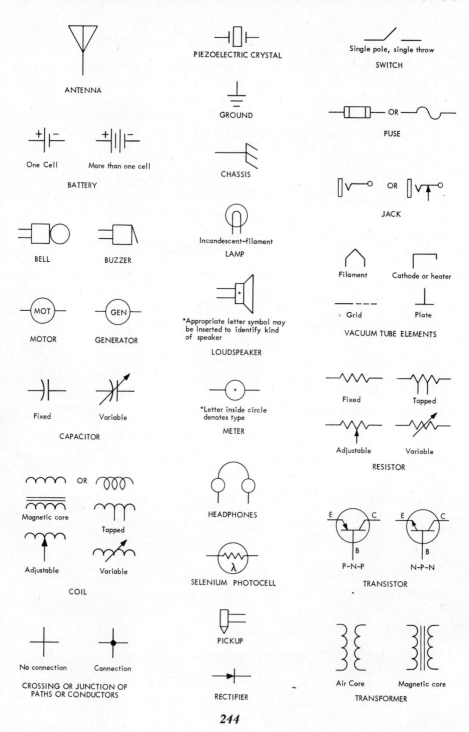

ANTENNA

PIEZOELECTRIC CRYSTAL

Single pole, single throw
SWITCH

One Cell   More than one cell
BATTERY

GROUND

OR
FUSE

CHASSIS

JACK

BELL   BUZZER

Incandescent–filament
LAMP

Filament   Cathode or heater

MOTOR   GENERATOR

*Appropriate letter symbol may
be inserted to identify kind
of speaker
LOUDSPEAKER

Grid   Plate
VACUUM TUBE ELEMENTS

Fixed   Variable
CAPACITOR

*Letter inside circle
denotes type
METER

Fixed   Tapped

Adjustable   Variable
RESISTOR

Magnetic core

Tapped

Adjustable   Variable
COIL

HEADPHONES

SELENIUM PHOTOCELL

E   C   E   C

B   B
P-N-P   N-P-N
TRANSISTOR

No connection   Connection
CROSSING OR JUNCTION OF
PATHS OR CONDUCTORS

PICKUP

RECTIFIER

Air Core   Magnetic core
TRANSFORMER

244

SOLDERING HINTS

In all electrical work, good soldering joints are essential. Solder is intended to provide a good electrical contact, to prevent corrosion at the joint, and to add strength to the joint or splice. Most electrical soldering is done with an electric soldering iron or a soldering gun.

Procedures for Soldering

1. Clean the Soldering Tip

When using an electric soldering iron, it is advisable to remove the copper tip from the iron before filing. File the tip as shown in Illustration 1 so that the four sides of the copper are smooth and come together to a point. The tip should be taken out of the iron at least once a week so that the corrosion can be removed from the copper. If the tip remains in the iron for long periods of time, it will corrode in the iron barrel. Should this occur, it is very difficult to ever remove the tip.

The soldering gun tip should be cleaned with steel wool or with sandpaper.

2. Tin the Tip

Heat the tip and then apply a thin coat of rosin core solder. Sometimes the solder will not stick even though the tip looks clean. When this occurs, rub the heated point with steel wool and again apply the rosin core solder. The tip should now be tinned and will have a shiny appearance. If excess solder remains on the tip, it can be removed by wiping the point with a rag.

3. Use Rosin Core Solder

Wire-shaped solder with a hollow core filled with rosin flux is recommended for all electrical connections. Acid core solder or paste fluxes are not desirable because they corrode connections.

4. All Parts to be Soldered Must be Clean

Solder will not stick to wire or terminals that have not been cleaned. Lugs, wires, and other parts to be soldered should be scraped with a knife until the metal appears bright. Thin wires covered with enamels can best be cleaned with sandpaper as shown in Illustration 2.

5. Make a Good Mechanical Connection

◆ 1. The copper soldering iron tip should be filed.

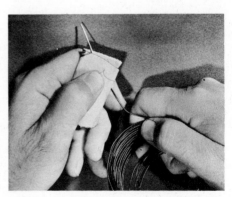

◆ 2. The insulation on small wires can be removed with sandpaper.

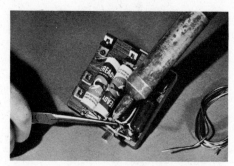

◆ 3. To conduct heat away from transistors the leads should be held with pliers when soldering.

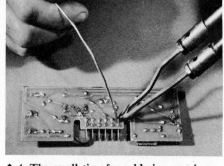

◆ 4. The small tip of a soldering gun is preferred when soldering printed circuits.

Before soldering, the wires should first be wrapped around terminals or securely clamped. After the wire is tight and secure, the solder can be applied.

6. Heat the Connection

The hot iron tip should be held against the parts to be joined until they are heated. Enough heat should be applied so that the solder melts when it touches the wires being joined together. The solder will then flow freely over and through the joint.

7. Keep the Connection from Moving

While the joint is being soldered and while the solder is cooling, the connection should be held perfectly still. Movement of the connection will result in a cold solder joint that may have a high resistance.

8. Use the Proper Amount of Solder

Use only enough solder to do the job.

Excessive solder does not help the connection, and this extra solder may cause a short circuit. If excessive solder appears, re-heat the joint and remove the extra solder by wiping it with a rag.

9. Protect Certain Parts from Heat

Certain parts such as diodes and transistors can easily be damaged by excessive heat. To avoid ruining these parts when soldering, the leads should be gripped with pliers as shown in Illustration 3. The pliers will conduct the heat away from the part.

10. For Small Spaces Use a Small Tip

Crowded electronic circuits may have a number of components in a very small space. A large soldering tip can easily damage the parts or the other connections. In such instances, a small tip such as found on soldering guns should be used. See Figure 4.

SUPPLEMENTARY PROJECTS

The following four projects are included in the appendix for use by the instructor as deemed most profitable for his particular class.

MAKING A MAGNETIC FIELD PATTERN DEVELOPER

Materials needed:

1 Tin can (size of 3 lb. shortening can or a 2 lb. coffee can)
1 Lamp socket
6 ft Lamp cord
1 ft Wood dowel, ¼″
1 Wood base
2 Pieces wood for can support
2 Pieces wood for pattern platform
1 Piece heavy cardboard
1 Attachment plug
1 Rubber grommet, ⅜″

◆ 1. Sprinkling steel wool on the wax paper held under the lamp of the magnetic field pattern developer.

Make a platform approximately 3″ high with two pieces of wood and a piece of heavy cardboard and secure it to the wood base. In securing the parts of the platform together and to the wood base, use glue instead of nails or screws. Mount the lamp socket on a wood block and drill a ¼″ hole lengthwise through the center of the block for the wood dowel. Drill two ¼″ holes through the sides of the can near the bottom, so that the piece of wood dowel can be inserted in the holes, and through the hole in the wood block which holds the lamp socket. Glue the piece of wood dowel to the wood block and secure the lamp socket to the bottom of the can. Drill a ¼″ hole in each of the can supports so that when the can is mounted and rotated the edge of the can will clear the top of the pattern platform by ¼″. Drill a ⅜″ hole in the bottom of the can near the lamp socket for the rubber grommet. Attach one end of the lamp cord to the lamp socket, extend the cord through the grommet and attach a plug cap on the opposite end. Insert a lamp in the socket and the field pattern developer is ready to operate. The size of the lamp may vary from 75 to 150 watts, depending upon the type of wax paper used in making the patterns.

To make a permanent magnetic field pattern, place a magnet, either permanent or electromagnetic, under the platform and close to the cardboard top. Place a piece of waxed paper on top of the platform and sprinkle fine iron filings on the paper. Pieces of steel wool rubbed together will produce very satisfactory results. Tap the cardboard top of the platform gently un-

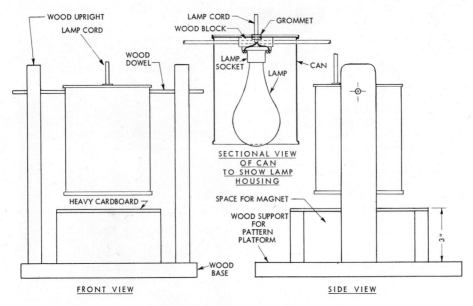

◆ 2. Magnetic Field Pattern Developer

til the desired pattern is formed, then swing the can with the lamp lighted over the pattern. Within one minute the heat from the lamp will cause the filings or pieces of steel wool to sink into the wax on the paper. When the heated lamp is removed a permanent pattern of the magnetic field will remain on the waxed paper.

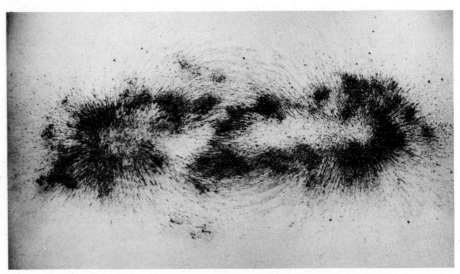

◆ 3. The magnetic pattern is permanently impressed on the wax paper.

PISTON TYPE MOTOR

Materials required:

2 Fiber washers, $\frac{1}{8}''$ thick, $1\frac{1}{8}''$ diameter
1 Piece wood dowel, $\frac{3}{8}'' \times 2''$
1 Piece soft steel, round, $\frac{1}{4}''$ diameter, $2\frac{1}{4}''$ long
1 Piece steel, round, $\frac{1}{8}''$ diameter, $3\frac{1}{4}''$ long
1 Piece sheet brass, $\frac{1}{16}''$ thick, $\frac{1}{4}'' \times 1\frac{1}{2}''$
2 Pieces sheet steel, 18 gage, $1\frac{1}{2}'' \times 2\frac{1}{2}''$
1 Piece brass rod, round, $\frac{1}{2}''$ diameter, $\frac{3}{16}''$ long
1 Piece spring brass, 26 gage, $\frac{3}{16}'' \times 2\frac{3}{4}''$
1 Piece wood, $\frac{3}{4}'' \times 1\frac{1}{2}'' \times 2''$
1 Piece wood, $\frac{1}{2}'' \times 4'' \times 6''$
2 Terminal screws
100 ft Magnet wire, No. 22, enam.
1 Flywheel (see text)

This type motor has an action somewhat like a steam engine in that the power is supplied to the flywheel by a piston moving back and forth. Make a coil form by drilling a $1\frac{7}{64}''$ hole through the piece of wood dowel and place a fiber washer at each end of the dowel. Drill two small holes in one washer for the coil leads and wind eight layers of No. 22 magnet wire on the form. Shape one end of the wood block to match the curve of the coil and glue the coil to the block. Secure the coil mount to the wood base with screws or glue in the approximate position shown in the assembly view. Shape and drill the piece of sheet brass to serve as the connecting rod.

File away one end of the piston rod so that the end of the connecting rod will fit against it and drill and tap the end of the rod as shown on the drawing for the piston. Secure the connecting rod to the piston with a 6-32 machine screw. Tighten the screw so that the connecting rod can move freely, then solder the end of the machine screw to the piston. The flywheel may be

◆ **4. Piston Type Motor**

turned from wood with a piece of pipe serving as a rim to give it weight, or it may be made by casting plaster of Paris in a jar lid, as was done with the motor shown in the photograph. Bend the piece of steel rod as shown in the drawing to serve as the crankshaft. Drill, shape, and bend the two pieces of sheet steel for the bearing stands, as shown in the drawing.

Assemble the crankshaft, flywheel, and bearing stands by first placing a 6-32 machine screw nut that has been drilled out to $\frac{1}{8}''$ over the straight end of the shaft. Next place a bearing stand on the shaft, then the flywheel, and finally, the other bearing stand and another drilled out machine screw nut. Place the whole assembly on the wood base and insert the end of the crankshaft through the hole in the connecting rod. Line up all of the parts so

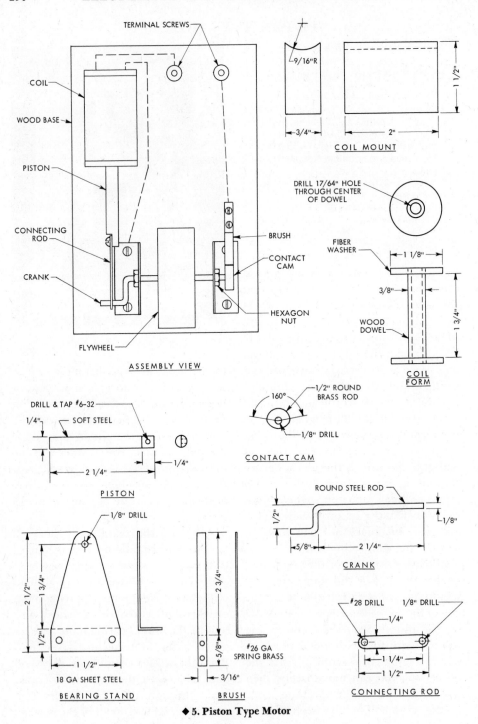

TERMINAL SCREWS

COIL

WOOD BASE

PISTON

CONNECTING ROD

CRANK

FLYWHEEL

ASSEMBLY VIEW

BRUSH

CONTACT CAM

HEXAGON NUT

COIL MOUNT

9/16"R

3/4"

2"

1 1/2"

DRILL 17/64" HOLE THROUGH CENTER OF DOWEL

FIBER WASHER

WOOD DOWEL

COIL FORM

1 1/8"

3/8"

1 3/4"

DRILL & TAP #6-32

SOFT STEEL

1/4"

2 1/4"

1/4"

PISTON

160°

1/2" ROUND BRASS ROD

1/8" DRILL

CONTACT CAM

ROUND STEEL ROD

1/2"

1/8"

5/8"

2 1/4"

CRANK

1/8" DRILL

2 1/2"

1 3/4"

1/2"

1 1/2"

18 GA SHEET STEEL

BEARING STAND

2 3/4"

5/8"

#26 GA SPRING BRASS

3/16"

BRUSH

#28 DRILL

1/8" DRILL

1/4"

1 1/4"

1 1/2"

CONNECTING ROD

◆ **5. Piston Type Motor**

that the moving parts work freely, then secure the bearing stands to the base with wood screws. Secure the flywheel to the shaft so that it will be centered between the bearings. Solder the machine screw nuts to the shaft to keep the flywheel centered.

Shape the piece of round brass rod to provide a cam approximately 160 degrees wide as shown in the drawing and place it on the end of the shaft. Drill and shape the piece of spring brass to serve as the brush, as shown in the drawing, and secure it to the wood base so that its end will rest against the contact cam. Adjust the cam so that it makes contact with the brush slightly after the piston begins its backward stroke and breaks contact with the brush just before the piston begins its forward stroke. In some instances the edges of the cam may need further dressing with a file to provide maximum operating results. Solder the cam to the shaft when it has been adjusted to the correct position. Wire the motor as shown in the assembly view and the motor will be ready to run. Direct current from 3 to 8 volts will operate the motor satisfactorily.

RADIO AND TELEVISION TUBE FILAMENT TESTER

Materials required:

1 Piece sheet steel, 20 gage, 5½″ x 6″
1 Resistor, 10,000 ohms
1 Neon lamp, NE-51
2 Octal sockets
2 Miniature sockets, 7 pin
1 Miniature socket, 9 pin
1 Rubber grommet, ¼″
1 Rubber grommet, ⅜″
6 ft Lamp cord
1 Attachment plug

One of the frequent causes of a radio or television receiver failing to operate is the burning out of one or more tube filaments. With this filament tester you can locate such tubes quickly and accurately. Tube manufacturers use different combinations as filament terminals for octal sockets and seven pin miniature sockets. Thus, two sockets of each type are provided to handle all present-day filament terminal arrangements. Since nine pin miniature tubes have only one filament terminal arrangement at present, only one such type tube socket is required.

Lay out, shape, and drill the piece

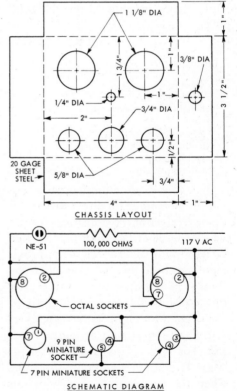

CHASSIS LAYOUT

SCHEMATIC DIAGRAM

◆ **6. Diagram of Radio and Television Tube Filament Tester**

of sheet steel as shown in the drawing. Bend the sides and ends of the chassis along the dotted lines and solder the corners together. Attach the tube sockets to the chassis in the holes provided. Secure a rubber grommet in the hole in the top of the chassis and press the neon lamp into the grommet with the terminals inside the chassis. Wire the tester according to the schematic diagram and attach the line cord after passing it through a rubber grommet in the end of the chassis. When testing either an octal base or a seven pin miniature tube, first place the tube in the socket on the left side, then in the socket on the right side. If the neon lamp lights in either case, the tube

◆ 7. **Radio and Television Tube Filament Tester**

filament is good. If the neon lamp fails to light, the filament is defective. To test a nine pin miniature tube, place it in the socket and observe the neon lamp as directed above.

TRANSISTOR AMPLIFIER

Materials required:

- 1 Piece wood, $\frac{1}{2}$″ x 3″ x 3″
- 1 Transistor, Raytheon CK 722
- 1 Fixed capacitor, electrolytic, 10 μf, 25 volts
- 1 Resistor (see text) R_1
- 1 Resistor, 220,000 ohms, R_2
- 2 Penlight cells
- 4 Fahnestock clips

This transistor amplifier will provide more volume for either the crystal diode receiver or the transistor receiver which are described elsewhere in this book. Mount the parts in the approximate position on the wood base as shown in Photograph 8. Wire the set according to Diagram 9. Two of the Fahnestock clips should be marked *input* and two should be marked *output*. For best results the value of resistor R_1 should be about 470 ohms when the amplifier is used with the transistor receiver and about 47,000

◆ 8. **Transistor Amplifier**

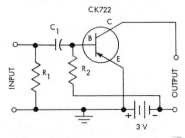

◆ 9. **Wiring Diagram of Transistor Amplifier**

ohms when it is used with the crystal diode receiver. To reduce current drain from the pen light cells, the head-phones or speaker should be discon-nected from the output side of the amplifier when it is not in use.

INDEX